THE
MENTAL
STATUS
EXAM

EXPLAINED
THIRD EDITION

David J. Robinson MD, FRCPC

Distinguished Fellow of the American Psychiatric Association
Fellow of the Canadian Psychiatric Association

Rapid Psychler® Press 👓

2014 Holland Avenue
#374
Port Huron, Michigan
USA 48060-1406

11-1673 Richmond Street
PMB 203
London, Ontario
Canada N6G 2N3

Toll Free Phone   888-PSY-CHLE (888-779-2453)
Toll Free Fax   888-PSY-CHLR (888-779-2457)
Outside the U.S. & Canada — Fax (1)519-675-0610
website   www.psychler.com
email   rapid@psychler.com

ISBN 978-1-894328-31-9
© 2017, Rapid Psychler Press, Third Edition, First Printing
Printed in the United States of America

All caricatures are fictitious. Any resemblance to real people either living or deceased is entirely coincidental (and unfortunate). The author assumes no responsibility for the consequences of diagnoses made nor treatment instituted as a result of the contents of this book. Only qualified mental health professionals should make such determinations. Every effort was made to ensure that the information in this book was accurate at the time of publication. Due to the changing nature of the field of psychiatry, the reader is encouraged to consult sources of information that are as current as possible.

Dedication

This book is dedicated to my partner in all things, my wife —

Jennifer Longard Robinson

Acknowledgments

I am indebted to the following individuals for their support:

- Jennifer Robinson
- Monty & Lil Robinson
- Brian Chapman
- Luis F. Ramirez MD

Rapid Psychler® Press ◯◯

produces books and presentation media that are:

✓ comprehensively researched
✓ well organized
✓ formatted for ease of use
✓ reasonably priced
✓ clinically oriented, and
✓ include humor as an enhancement to education.

Table of Contents

1. Introduction to the Mental Status Exam

What is the Mental Status Examination?

The **Mental Status Examination (MSE)** is the component of an interview where cognitive functions are tested and inquiries are made about the symptoms of psychiatric conditions. It is a set of standardized observations and questions designed to evaluate:

- **Sensorium**
- **Perception**
- **Thinking**
- **Feeling**
- **Behavior**

The MSE is an integral part of any clinical interview, not just one that takes place in a psychiatric context. An assessment of cognitive functions must be made before information from patients can be considered reliable and accurate. The MSE records only observed behavior, cognitive abilities and inner experiences expressed during the interview. It is conducted to assess as completely as possible the factors necessary to arrive at a preferred diagnosis, formulate a treatment plan and follow a patient's clinical course. The MSE is a portable assessment tool that helps identify psychiatric symptoms and gauge their severity. With experience it is a specific, sensitive and inexpensive diagnostic instrument. The MSE takes only a few minutes to administer yet yields information that is crucial for making a diagnostic assessment and initiating or modifying a course of treatment.

What Are the Components of the MSE?

The MSE can be thought of as a psychiatric "review of symptoms." Assessing the five main areas listed above provides essential information for developing a differential diagnosis and a treatment plan. Expanding on these five domains yields the entire scope of what is assessed and recorded in the MSE.

Sensorium & Cognitive Functions

- Level of consciousness and attentiveness
- Orientation to person, place and time
- Attention
- Concentration
- Memory
- Knowledge (estimation)
- Intelligence (estimation)
- Capacity for abstract thinking

Perception

- Disorders of sensory input where there is no stimulus (hallucinations), where a stimulus is misperceived (illusions), or of altered bodily experiences (depersonalization or derealization)

Thinking

- Speech
- Thought Content (*what* is said)
- Thought Form (*how* something is said or *the way* it is said)
- Suicidal & Homicidal Ideation
- Insight & Judgment

Feeling

- Affect (objective, visible emotional cues)
- Mood (subjective, emotional experience)

Behavior

- Appearance
- Agitation or reduction of movement
- Degree of cooperation with the interview process

How Do I Remember All That?

The following memory aid* not only lists the main areas, it does so in the order that they are usually asked about and presented.

"ABC STAMP LICKER" *

Appearance
Behavior
Cooperation

Speech
Thought — form and content
Affect — moment-to-moment variation in emotion
Mood — subjective emotional tone during the interview
Perception — in all sensory modalities

Level of Consciousness
Insight & Judgment
Cognitive Functions & Sensorium
    Orientation
    Memory
    Attention & Concentration
    Reading & Writing
Knowledge base — general knowledge
Endings — suicidal and/or homicidal ideation
Reliability of the information provided

* **"ABC STAMP LICKER"**
mnemonic/memory aid
© David J. Robinson MD

Do I Have to Conduct an MSE?

The **American Psychiatric Association (APA)** Practice Guidelines lists the MSE as a core component for psychiatric evaluations (APA, 2016). It is as essential to a complete psychiatric assessment as physical examinations are in other areas of medicine. The MSE has also been referred to as a "brain stethoscope" (O'Neill, 1993).

All psychiatric diagnoses are made clinically in interview situations. There is no blood test, imaging study or single identifying feature for any psychiatric condition. This highlights the necessity of a thorough assessment of which the MSE is an essential component. The MSE is often unpopular for two reasons:

- Questions are difficult to formulate because they are not asked in other types of interviews or in other areas of medicine, nursing, psychology, etc.
- Questions appear to be of dubious relevance to novice interviewers

Once these two difficulties are surmounted, the MSE becomes an enjoyable and interesting aspect of interviewing. To achieve this level of comfort, it helps to realize that almost half of the MSE is obtained "free" — that is, through observing the patient and listening to what is being said in other parts of the interview.

Free Parameters	Parameters to Ask About
Level of Consciousness	Orientation
Appearance	Cognitive Functions
Behavior	Suicidal/Homicidal Thoughts
Cooperation	General Knowledge
Reliability	Perception
Affect	Mood
Thought Form	Thought Content

How Do I Start the MSE?

The MSE begins as soon as the patient is within your view. A moment of observation before the interview begins already reveals important information such as: grooming, hygiene, behavior, gait, level of interest in and interaction with the surroundings, etc.

Other elements of the MSE are obtained as the assessment proceeds. Most interviewers begin interviews with open-ended questions and allow patients a few moments of relatively unstructured time to "tell their story."

Invariably there are items in the MSE that will have to be specifically asked about, and this can be done in one of three ways:

1. Take the opportunity when the chance arises in the interview to ask about items from the MSE. This is the most natural approach and allows the MSE to be intertwined with the body of the interview. For example, many patients will complain of having a poor memory and a decreased attention span, which presents an ideal opportunity to test cognitive functions. The disadvantage to this approach is that it can disrupt the structure of the interview. For those new to interviewing and to the MSE this technique may be better left until more experience has been gained in recording information that is out of sequence with the typical interview format.

2. Take note of key points in the history that allow you to make a smooth transition back to them at some point later on. For example, *"You mentioned before that your hearing was affected. Did this ever cause you to hear something unusual or that others couldn't hear?"* This lets patients know that they have been listened to while allowing you to stick to a more structured interview style. If patients say something that introduces an important area but at an inopportune time you can say something like, *"It's important for me to know about that, and we'll get back to it in a few minutes, but right now could you tell me more about what we were just discussing. . ."* (just remember to ask about it later!).

3. Ask about the areas that remain unexamined at the end of the interview. This too has the advantage of helping preserve the structure of the interview. While the two previous approaches are more elegant, there aren't always opportunities to use them. The remaining sections of the MSE can be formally introduced as follows:

"At this point, I'd like to ask you some questions that are separate from what we've been discussing but will give me more important information about you."

> or

"Right now, I'd like to ask you some questions to give me an idea about some aspects of your experiences and functioning that we haven't covered yet."

> or

"There are some other areas that I need to formally test to get an idea about your...(concentration, attention, etc.)."

> or

"In order to be as thorough as possible, I need to ask you some questions about your mental functions and inner experiences."

These questions are only suggestions, so do ask instructors or colleagues for their own preferred phrases. While conducting the MSE is essential, it can be done in a variety of ways and the components may be obtained in any order. Draw on the experiences of others initially with a view to developing your own approach. As you become increasingly more comfortable with the process, some day you may actually get to write your own book about the MSE!

Specific questions regarding certain sections of the MSE (e.g. hallucinations and delusions) are included in their respective chapters.

Integration of the History and the MSE

Psychiatric History   **MSE Component**

Identifying Data &
Chief Complaint
- **Appearance**
- **Behavior**
- **Orientation**
  (ask patients for their full
  names, if they had difficulty
  finding the clinic/hospital, etc.)
- **Level of Consciousness (LOC)**

History of Present Illness (HPI)
2 to 5 minutes of
relatively unstructured
time using open-
ended questions and
other facilitating
techniques
- **Cooperation**
- **Thought Form**
- **Thought Content**
  (this format allows patients to talk
  about what concerns them, a
  valuable indicator of thought
  content)

Exploration of
Symptoms from HPI
A more focused assess-
ment with elaboration
of material from the
HPI using closed-
ended questions
to get more specific
information
- **Affect**
- **Mood**
- **Suicidal/Homicidal Ideation**
- **Elements of Cognitive
  Functioning** (it may be helpful
  to include certain tests at this point
  to gauge the severity of reported
  symptoms (e.g. concentration))

Direct Testing of Other
MSE Components
For the areas that are not
amenable to exploration
earlier in the interview
- **General Knowledge**
- **Perception**
- **Insight & Judgment**
- **Formal Cognitive Testing**

How Else Can I Conceptualize the MSE?

The MSE can be considered the "physical examination" of psychiatry. Eliciting somatic symptoms in physical medicine warrants examination of the affected areas via the **I.P.P.A.** approach:

- **I**nspection
- **P**alpation
- **P**ercussion
- **A**uscultation

Further "looking into," "touching on," "sounding out," and "listening to" is required to fully evaluate psychiatric symptoms. Unlike the physical exam, the MSE is at least partly integrated with the psychiatric history. Like the physical exam, the MSE is recorded separately from the body of the history.

The MSE can also be considered part of the *objective* portion of the **S.O.A.P.** approach to recording information:

- **Subjective**   Consists of sections from the interview:
  Chief Complaint
  History of Present Illness
  Medical and Psychiatric History
  Family and Personal History

- **Objective**   Recording of observations:
  Mental Status Exam
  Physical Examination
  Laboratory Testing

- **Assessment**   Provisional/Preferred Diagnosis
  & Differential Diagnoses

- **Plan**   Further Investigations,
  Short-Term and Longer-Term Treatment

MSE Practice Points

• The **Mini-Mental State Examination (MMSE)** is NOT the same as a complete MSE. The MMSE is a structured bedside test of various cognitive functions that is scored out of a maximum of 30 points. There are many aspects of a complete MSE that are not dealt with in the MMSE, such as perceptual disturbances, thought process and content disturbances, affect and mood, etc.

M. Folstein, S. Folstein & P. McHugh
Mini-Mental State: A Practical Method for Grading the Cognitive State of Patients for the Clinician.
Journal of Psychiatric Research 12: p. 189 – 198, 1975

• The MSE is an evaluation of the patient at the time of the interview. The findings on the MSE can and do change (invariably in front of a senior colleague). *It is a record of observations made only during a particular assessment.*

• The MSE provides an assessment to help monitor course and prognosis. It has a high test-retest value and reveals essential information about a patient's clinical course.

• The MSE consists of a relatively standardized approach and set of inquiries, though many clinicians have a rationale for doing things a certain way and possibly in a certain order.

• Performing and recording a complete MSE is one of the most important steps a clinician can take to avoid malpractice actions (or at least limiting one's liability). Many medical communications periodicals (i.e. *Psychiatric News*, *Psychiatric Times*) have reported that lawsuits were dropped or damages minimized because the documented MSE supported a clinician's course of action.

• The MSE is an integral component of competence/capacity assessments. **Competence** refers to having the ability to understand and act reasonably; it is a legal term and the decision about someone's competence is made by a judge. **Capacity** is the mental ability to make rational decisions based on understanding and appreciating all relevant information; it is determined by a clinician.

2. Appearance

Which Aspects of Appearance Are Important?

Recording information about appearance provides a mental picture of the physical characteristics of a patient. This is done not only to develop an accurate record but to convey to others as closely as possible what it was like to be with the person. Features of appearance that are important are:

- **Gender & Cultural Background** (Section I)
- **Actual & Apparent Age** (II)
- **Attire** (III)
- **Grooming & Hygiene** (IV)
- **Body Habitus** (V)
- **Physical Abnormalities** (VI)
- **Jewelry & Cosmetic Use** (VII)
- **Other Features** (tattoos, body piercing, scars, unusual pattern of hair loss, etc.) (VIII)

How is Appearance Described?

I — **Gender** and **Cultural Background** are basic descriptive features.

II — **Actual Age** is factual identifying information. **Apparent Age** is an assessment made by the interviewer based on actual age and other factors such as the condition of the patient's hair and skin, style of clothing and behavior. Apparent age is often recorded as:

- *Appears his or her stated age*
- *Appears younger/older than the stated age*

Many factors can contribute to an aged appearance, such as:

- Serious and/or prolonged physical illnesses
- Exposure to the elements (weather)/homelessness
- Smoking, alcohol or other substance abuse
- Chronic and/or severe psychiatric disorders

<u>**III**</u> — **Attire** describes how patients are dressed and how they have presented themselves for the interview. Attire is a reflection of many factors: socioeconomic status, occupation, self-esteem, ability and interest in attending to contemporary styles, etc. Descriptions often include a comment on overall impression and then the details of how patients are dressed, e.g. *"The patient was meticulously dressed in a tuxedo with a top hat and white gloves…"*

Due consideration must be given to the circumstances of the interview. An inpatient who woke up five minutes prior to an impromtu interview warrants a different level of expectation than does an executive attending a planned outpatient appointment.

It is prudent to keep in mind that medical records are legal documents. Your comments can surface again in a variety of settings, with the courtroom being one of the most common. Patients also have the right to read their medical records. For this reason, descriptions are best made with regard to the congruity of patients' attire to the context of the interview, followed by a basic, factual description. For example:

Right: *"This man was dressed as if prepared for the outdoors. He had on a fur trader's hat, and a jacket worn over a striped shirt."*

Wrong: *"This rube had on a très gauche, fake raccoon fur hat and a cheap-looking sweater worn over an Ernie (of Bert & Ernie) style undershirt."*

Attire, when taken in context with other signs and symptoms, can provide useful information. For example:

- During manic episodes, patients may dress flamboyantly and often show a preference for bright colors

- Schizophrenia, depression, dementia and substance misuse are common causes for declining interest in self-care (e.g. attire, grooming, hygiene, etc.)
- Patients with personality disorders can reflect important character traits in their choice of clothing
- Patients suffering from anorexia often dress in loose, baggy clothing to hide their state of emaciation
- Intravenous drug users may wear long-sleeve shirts to hide needle marks (often referred to as "tracks")

IV — Grooming & Hygiene are indicators that reflect a patient's level of self-care. Hair, attention to facial hair, skin condition, nails, body odor, oral hygiene and condition of clothing are the major aspects surveyed. Common descriptions are:

- *Disheveled* (ruffled as if by a strong wind)
- *Unkempt* (poor attention to grooming)
- *Immaculately, neatly, adequately* or *poorly groomed* are other common descriptive terms used

As with attire, the level of grooming and hygiene can help to make a diagnosis and gauge the severity of a psychiatric condition:

- Patients with **Obsessive-compulsive disorder (OCD)** may wash so frequently that they cause skin damage
- Delusional disorders can affect the level of grooming (e.g. not washing to ward off a feared entity)
- Patients with an **Obsessive-compulsive** or **narcissistic personality disorder** are often fastidiously groomed and spend a considerable amount of time on their appearance
- Chronic, severe mental illnesses in general reduce the level to which patients maintain their self-care

V — Body Habitus refers to the patient's build or body type. To help convey an accurate image, descriptions can be made using the following terms:

- *Ectomorphic:* thin or slight body build
- *Mesomorphic:* muscular or sturdy build
- *Endomorphic:* heavy or portly body build

Unusual body proportions should be noted, for example:

- Truncal obesity with wasting of the arms and legs occurs in Cushing's disease/syndrome and liver disease
- A barrel chest that is disproportionate to the rest of the body can be caused by emphysema or chronic bronchitis

VI — Physical Abnormalities should be noted as well as the resulting handicap and the need for any assistive devices. In social situations it is often polite and tactful to avoid discussing handicaps, but exploring these areas during the interview is important for completing the MSE. A sensitive line of questioning indicating your interest will help explore these areas. The following inquiries can act as a guide:

- Is the missing/disfigured part a congenital or an acquired condition?
- If congenital, what difficulties did this pose during development?
- If acquired, was it through an accident? An assault? An attempt at self-harm?
- What limitations does the disability cause?
- How has the patient adjusted to the loss?
- What are the psychological consequences *to this person* regarding the physical impairment?

Exploring these areas also conveys to patients that you are willing to discuss any aspect of their lives and this creates a greater degree of openness in the interview. Physical handicaps can be significant for the following reasons:

- The level of adjustment gives a good idea of someone's

overall ability to cope with stressors and losses; the ability to adapt gives a good indication of level of insight and the ability to exercise good judgment
- Relevance to the cause/etiology of psychiatric disorders

VII — Jewelry and **Cosmetic Use** are extensions of attire and grooming, respectively. They can convey a sense of how patients see themselves and what they consider important. Examples of the usefulness of these observations are as follows:

- Makeup can be bizarrely applied by patients with psychotic conditions and lavishly by patients who are manic or who have certain personality disorders
- Patients with schizophrenia or schizotypal personality disorder may wear amulets or trinkets to which they have attached some mystical or highly personal significance

The study of rings is a fascinating pastime. In addition to marital status they can indicate things like occupation (e.g. engineers wear a steel or iron ring on the fifth finger of their working hand).

VIII — Tattoos

Tattoos are applied by the injection of indelible ink into the dermal layer of the skin. They have achieved an unprecedented level of popularity (especially since the first edition of this book!). Many celebrities flaunt them. There are conventions, magazines, associations and renowned artists all making tattooing a culture unto itself. Tattoos reflect a myriad of meanings. For example, they can signify membership in criminal organizations or convictions for certain crimes. Alternatively they can be expressions of attachment to a person or lifestyle (e.g. sexual orientation or sexual practices). People seek to express themselves through their appearance and tattoo wearers have used their skin as a canvas with which to make a permanent and highly personal statement. It is important (and interesting) to ask about tattoos even if they are not visible.

Questions that you might ask of patients are:

- *"What is the tattoo? What does it represent?"*
- *"What was going on in your life when you got the tattoo?"*
- *"What made this person/group/event so significant to you?"*
- *"What gave you the…(confidence/hope/etc.) that you would always feel as strongly towards the…(person/organization/etc.)?"*
- *"Have you ever regretted getting tattoos? Have you taken any steps to have them removed?"*

From these questions, you can learn about:

- Significant relationships, level of commitment, etc.
- Affiliation with groups, subcultures, etc.
- Sexual practices, legal involvement, etc.
- Level of impulse control, insight, judgment, etc.

Isn't It Judgmental to Make Inferences About a Patient's Appearance?

Appearance is too important a feature not to include in the MSE. While inferences can be drawn and hypotheses made regarding certain features, further information is of course required for confirmation. Diagnostic impressions are based on more that just appearance. People adapt their grooming styles to express themselves by wearing certain clothing, jewelry and cosmetics. In interview situations clinicians strive to interpret more than fashion statements. A wealth of information is available to experienced observers. To illustrate this, consider the famous Victorian detective Sherlock Holmes (Conan Doyle, 1971). In the short story called *The Yellow Face*, he examines a pipe and tells Dr. Watson *"the owner is obviously a muscular man, left-handed, with an excellent set of teeth, careless in his habits, and with no need to practice economy."* How Holmes arrives at these conclusions makes perfect sense once he reveals both his observations and their significance. Holmes is an inspiration to those wishing to enhance their observational and deductive skills.

Some "Psychiatric" Physical Findings

Head & Neck

- Altered pupil size   drug intoxication/withdrawal
- Corneal pigmentation   Wilson's disease
- Dental caries   eating disorders (from vomiting)
- Parotid enlargement   anorexia/bulimia nervosa

Skin

- Callus/laceration   eating disorder (due to self-induced
  on knuckles   vomiting)
- Scars from self-cutting   borderline personality disorder
- Scars from trauma   antisocial personality;
                             substance misuse
- Needle marks/tracks   IV drug use
- Cigarette burns   dementia; substance misuse; other
                             neurologic conditions; self harm
- Dermatitis or   OCD — compulsive hand wash-
  excoriated skin   ing; may occur on knees from
                            cleaning in a kneeling position
- Unusual pattern of   trichotillomania (repeated pulling
  hair loss   out of hair)
- Lanugo hair   anorexia nervosa
- Café-au-lait macules   neurofibromatosis
- Edema   medications; anorexia nervosa

Musculoskeletal & Nervous System

- Tremor   Parkinson's disease, lithium use,
                            caffeine intoxication, alcohol
                            withdrawal, anxiety disorders,
                            hyperthyroidism
- Repeated movements   Tourette's disorder, tic disorders,
                            autism, tardive dyskinesia,
                            obsessive-compulsive disorder,
                            mental retardation
- Muscle wasting   alcohol misuse (chronic)

3. Behavior

Which Aspects of Behavior Are Important?

Behavior refers to activity during the interview and is one of the cardinal means of classifying mental illness. It provides outwardly observable manifestations of psychiatric conditions. Patients may be delusional, suicidal or plagued by hallucinations, but these are internal experiences to which clinicians have no direct access. Behavior reveals information about other parameters of the MSE such as: mood, cooperation & reliability, thought content, etc. As with appearance the assessment of behavior begins the instant patients are within view, which may be the only opportunity to observe certain actions (e.g. tics, compulsions). The major aspects of behavior are:

General Observations
- **Agitation** (Section I)
- **Hyperactivity** (II)
- **Psychomotor Retardation** (III)

Observation of Specific Movements
- **Akathisia** (Section IV)
- **Automatisms** (V)
- **Catatonia** (VI)
- **Choreoathetoid Movements** (VII)
- **Compulsions** (VIII)
- **Dystonias** (IXa) & **Extrapyramidal Symptoms** (IXb)
- **Tardive Dyskinesia** (X)
- **Tics** (XI)
- **Tremors** (XII)
- **Negative Symptoms** (XIII)

Observation of behavior is the critical element in descriptive psychopathology. **Phenomenology** is the study and categorization of observed events without inferring causation. This was the initial basis for classifying mental disorders (as well as being a key concept in many other areas of endeavor, particularly philosophy).

How Do I Describe the General Aspects of Activity?

Activity level is a global description of patients' physical movements. Individual factors assessed are:

- Posture
- Range and frequency of spontaneous movements
- Cooperation and ability to carry out requested tasks

Activity level is generally recorded as:

- *Increased* (also referred to as agitated)
- *Decreased* or *slowed* (called hypokinesis or bradykinesis)
- *Within normal limits* (WNL)

Even in cases where there are no obvious behavioral abnormalities, a brief description provides a visual image of what it was like to be in the interview (e.g. *"Mr. YKK sat comfortably in the room with his arms folded across his chest and fiddled with the zipper on his jacket in an absent-minded fashion…"*)

A complete recording of movements involves three categories:

- **Conscious voluntary movements** — such as getting up to wipe fingerprints from a mirror
- **Unconscious voluntary movements** — such as adjusting eyeglasses or clearing one's throat; *Habits and Mannerisms* fall under this category
- **Involuntary movements** — such as tremors or dystonias; these are often neurological abnormalities

The Behavior Section of the MSE records only the observable actions, not the patient's internal experiences related to it (i.e. patients who constantly adjust their glasses may have a motor tic causing them to do this, but only the action is recorded in this section).

I — Agitation is described as physical restlessness with a heightened sense of tension and level of arousal. Common signs are:

- Hand wringing, finger tapping or fidgeting
- Frequent shifts in posture or position
- Foot tapping or rhythmic leg movements
- Frequent shifts in the focus of attention

Agitation can also be used to describe an emotional state or **affect** in that patients can both feel and appear agitated. **Psychomotor** refers to movements that are psychically determined as opposed to those caused by external sources. For example, a high caffeine intake can cause people to feel restless and agitated. This distinction is important because there are many causes of agitation (see the list below). In recognition of this the DSM-5 specifies **psychomotor agitation** in the diagnostic criteria for mania, hypomania and major depressive episodes. Agitation is seen in the following conditions:

- Substance ingestion/withdrawal
- General medical conditions such as hyperthyroidism, hypoparathyroidism, dementia and delirium
- Psychiatric conditions such as schizophrenia, depression, mania/hypomania, any of the anxiety disorders, and Cluster A & C personality disorders:
  Cluster A — Paranoid, Schizoid, Schizotypal
  Cluster B — Histrionic, Borderline, Antisocial, Narcissistic
  Cluster C — Obsessive-Compulsive, Dependent, Avoidant
- Agitated depression: patients may experience a combination of manic and depressive symptoms (**mixed features**); this is very unpleasant to endure and can lead to more suicide attempts or completions than other bipolar mood states

II — Hyperactivity refers to an increased level of physical energy. It is distinguished from agitation by the absence of inner tension and by the fact that the behaviors are usually goal directed.

Patients often speak quickly and at length, and may become unusually assertive or even aggressive. This is a common observation among patients suffering from:

- Mania or hypomania
- Attention-deficit/hyperactivity disorder (ADHD)
- Obsessive-compulsive personality disorder (OCPD)

An increased level of activity can also be seen in the following conditions:

- Catatonic excitement
- Seizure disorders, particularly during an interictal period
- Head injuries or delirium

III — Psychomotor retardation refers to the slowness of voluntary and involuntary movements. Other terms used to describe retardation are **hypokinesia** or **bradykinesia** and in extreme cases the virtual absence of movement is called **akinesia**. The term retardation applies to the initiation, execution and completion of movement. It excludes those who may have trouble starting tasks due to indecisiveness (but who are capable of completing them readily). Also excluded are those who start tasks easily but can't complete them because of poor concentration.

Often accompanying the slowed movements are changes in voice and **prosody of speech** (the natural emotional tone or inflection of speech). Most people move spontaneously when speaking and often gesture with their hands to facilitate speech or accentuate what they are saying. Other typical movements include adjusting eyeglasses, scratching, shifting posture, crossing and uncrossing legs, folding and unfolding arms, etc. Keeping track of a patient's repertoire of spontaneous movements is a valuable exercise. Make a point of asking about unusual or repetitive actions *and the absence of typical movements*. Descriptions of behavior must also be prefaced by an indication of the level of consciousness. You would not be surprised to hear that obtunded or comatose patients demonstrated severely diminished body movements (akinesia), but you'd most likely want to hear about their reduced level of consciousness first.

In general mental processes are slowed along with body movements, with patients reporting that they are unable to think as fast as they usually can. Such reports must be distinguished from **intellectual disability** (defects in intellectual functioning during the developmental period). The distinction is that patients who are intellectually disabled have permanent learning disabilities. Patients with dementia achieved a normal level of intelligence and then acquired an illness causing them to lose their mental faculties.

Depression can affect cognitive functioning so severely that the person appears to be demented. This was historically called **pseudodementia** or the **dementia syndrome of depression** (neither are official DSM-5 terms). While the latter term more accurately reflects the pathology of the process, pseudodementia is seen in other conditions (e.g. hypothyroidism) and is still a popular descriptive term. Causes for decreased or diminished movements are:

- Major depressive disorder, which is the most common psychiatric cause; in past diagnostic nomenclature there was a subtype of depression that was even called *retarded depression*
- Schizophrenia, particularly the presence of **deficit** or **negative symptoms**
- Medication side-effects, especially due to antipsychotics
- Catatonia
- Dementia of any cause
- General medical conditions

Specific Movement Abnormalities

IV — **Akathisia** is a state of inner tension to keep moving. It occurs most often as a side effect of psychiatric medication. Patients often seem ill at ease, move their legs rhythmically or have to get up and walk around the room. Akathisia cannot be differentiated from other states of agitation by observation alone — it is a subjective experience. It is called **neuroleptic-induced** when it is caused by antipsychotic medications. The usual manifestations are rocking, fidgeting, pacing or generally feeling compelled to keep moving. Akathisia can be quite uncomfortable. Suicides and assaults have been reported because it was not detected or adequately treated. Akathisia is often caused by starting or increasing the dosage of antipsychotic medication, or by decreasing or stopping agents that reduce its symptoms. Voluntary suppression of akathisia-driven movements only serves to increase the sense of discomfort.

<u>**V**</u> — **Automatisms** are "automatic" involuntary movements that can range from simple to complex behaviors. They occur most commonly in epileptic seizures of the partial complex or absence type. Automatisms may be the only outward manifestations of a seizure. They are also seen in head injuries, substance ingestion, catatonia, dissociative and fugue states. By definition, automatisms occur during an altered state of consciousness. During automatisms, actions can range from purposeful to disorganized and may or may not be appropriate for the situation or the person displaying them. Patients may remain partially aware of their surroundings. They may continue with their actions, but do not seem "quite right" at the time and are amnestic for the episode. Some automatisms are:

- Lip-smacking or uttering words
- Fumbling with clothing (especially buttons or zippers)
- Eye blinking or an unwavering stare

<u>**VI**</u> — **Catatonia** is a term applied to a diverse number of postural and movement disturbances. The movement disorders can include both increased and decreased levels of activity. The term catatonia was coined by Kahlbaum, and was initially a diagnostic entity on its own. If Kahlbaum had been a dog person, he would have called it dogatonia. Catatonia is also found in:

- Periodic catatonia, a rare variant which may involve alterations in thyroid function and nitrogen balance
- Neurologic illnesses
- Syphilis or viral encephalopathies
- Head trauma, arteriovenous malformations, etc.
- Toxic states and metabolic abnormalities

A mnemonic for many of the DSM-5 features of catatonia is:

"WRENCHES"

Weird movements (posturing, mannerisms, grimacing)
Rigidity
Echopraxia — copying someone's body movements
Negativism — automatic opposition to all requests
Catalepsy — waxy flexibility
High level of motor activity (agitation)
Echolalia — repeating the words of others
Stereotypy — repetitive abnormal movements

<u>**VII**</u> — **Choreoathetoid** movements are seen in various neurologic and psychiatric disorders. This is an amalgamation of two types of movement disorders, *choreiform* and *athetoid*.

Choreiform movements are involuntary and appear as irregular, jerky, spasmodic and quasi-purposeful; they are irregularly timed and generally not repeated. These movements most often affect the face and arms. An example of a choreiform movement is someone whose hand shoots up towards her face and then incorporates this gesture appearing like she is adjusting her hair.

Athetoid movements are slow, writhing (snake-like), twisting and have the appearance of following a pattern. Any muscle group can be affected. An athetoid movement might look like someone practicing Tai Chi or using their hand to imitate an airplane climbing and diving.

Ballismus is a larger-amplitude, faster and more violent motion. It usually occurs on one side of the body **(hemiballismus)** and resembles accelerated athetoid movements (like a punch into the air). The most common causes for these movements are:

- Huntington's chorea
- Sydenham's chorea (rheumatic fever)
- Wilson's disease (hepatolenticular degeneration)
- Multiple sclerosis
- Tourette's disorder

Causes of these abnormal movements in psychiatry are:

- Use of antiparkinsonian (dopaminergic) agents
- Use of stimulants (e.g. to treat ADHD)
- Use of anticonvulsants (e.g. phenytoin)
- Lithium toxicity
- Tardive dyskinesia **(TD)**

<u>VIII</u> — **Compulsions** are described in the DSM-5 as:

1. Repetitive behaviors or mental acts that the person feels driven to perform in response to an obsession, or according to rules that must be applied rigidly.
2. Behaviors or mental acts are aimed at preventing or reducing distress or preventing some dreaded event or situation; however, these behaviors or mental acts are either not considered to be realistically connected with what they are designed to neutralize or prevent, or are clearly excessive.

Two points require emphasis with this definition:
1. Compulsions can be mental experiences such as prayers or sayings, though the majority of compulsions are actions.
2. The "rules that must be applied rigidly" are self-imposed and not due to involvement with an organization with a strict code of conduct (e.g. mom, house arrest, etc.).

Compulsions are:

- Unwanted and **egodystonic** (insight is preserved)
- Purposeful or semi-purposeful actions that are performed to decrease anxiety
- Performed consciously
- Stereotyped (repeated over and over)
- Ritualistic (performed the same way each time)
- Usually linked to obsessions; e.g. obsessions about dirt often cause compulsions to clean things, etc.

Compulsions can occur alone, but are usually preceded by **obsessions** (recurrent thoughts, images or impulses) that are:

- Recurrent and recognized as unreasonable
- Not simply excessive concerns about realistic problems
- Recognized as coming from the person's mind as opposed to thoughts being inserted from elsewhere (from without)

A patient's current compulsions may or may not be evident in interview situations. Some patients can endure the anxiety that stems from suppressing compulsions for the duration of the time spent being observed. If compulsions are reported but not seen, they should be listed in the case presentation in the *History of Present Illness* or *Psychiatric History* section, but not in the MSE. The most common compulsions are:

- Excessive or ritualized grooming (hand washing, showering, brushing teeth, combing hair, etc.)
- Excessive cleaning of objects
- Repetition (e.g. dressing in a certain order)
- Checking (e.g. doors to see if they are locked)
- Counting, touching or measuring
- Ordering or arranging (usually in some apparent sequence, such as size, alphabetical order or symmetry)
- Hoarding or collecting

The following questions can help screen for compulsions:

- *"Are there actions that you perform repetitively?"*
- *"Do you spend time doing something over and over?"*
- *"Do you clean, check or arrange things on a repetitive basis?"*

<u>IXa</u> — **Dystonia** is an involuntary increase in muscle tone and one of the **extrapyramidal symptom (EPS)** side effects. Dystonias are manifested as sustained torsions or contractions of muscles (usually muscle groups) that give patients a contorted appearance. They generally occur in three circumstances:

- As a reaction to antipsychotic medications
- As a manifestation of schizophrenia
- As the consequence of a neurologic condition

Acute dystonias usually occur within the first several days of neuroleptic administration. Young males and patients who receive higher-potency neuroleptics (e.g. haloperidol) have a higher risk for these reactions. Some clinicians advocate that antiparkinsonian agents should be used prophylactically to prevent dystonias in higher-risk groups. Common dystonias are:

- **Oculogyric crisis** or **spasm** — fixed upward gaze or eye muscles forced into a dysconjugate gaze
- **Torticollis** or **wry neck** — a spasmodic contraction of neck muscles causing the head to rotate sideways or be held at an angle
- **Opisthotonos** — a spasm in the neck and back muscles that causes an arching backward; in severe cases recumbent patients have only their heels and the backs of their heads touching the floor
- **Laryngospasm** — a dystonia of the muscles controlling the tongue and throat; it can lead to difficulty speaking, swallowing and breathing

Dystonias are very uncomfortable and often frighting. The presence of a dystonic reaction requires immediate intervention. Prolonged reactions such as those listed above are a major reason why patients don't adhere to their medication regimen. Untreated these reactions can last well in excess of an hour. Fortunately dystonias can usually be treated both effectively and quickly with antiparkinsonian medications (such as benztropine).

Most acute dystonias seen in current practice are due to antipsychotic medication. However, dystonias have been documented in patients with schizophrenia who have never been exposed to neuroleptic medication. Not only have dystonic reactions been recorded, but a whole range of motor disorders have been seen including abnormalities in:

- Posture, tone and gait
- Eye movements and repeated blinking
- Facial, head, trunk and limb movements
- Speech production

Dystonias can also be **tardive** as opposed to acute. Next to **torticollis** the most common is **blepharospasm** (involuntary closure of the eyelids) though this often spreads as well to muscles controlling head movements and chewing. Dystonia itself is a neurologic condition and is differentiated from other motor disorders by the presence of repetitive, patterned and sustained movements that have no discernable psychiatric cause.

IXb — Other Extrapyramidal Symptoms (EPS)

The pyramidal tracts originate in the posterior frontal and anterior parietal lobes. Ninety percent of the fibers pass through the pyramid of the medulla and form a tract found laterally in the spinal cord. The group of nuclei, known as the **basal ganglia**, constitute the major component of the extrapyramidal system. The following is a list of extrapyramidal reactions (ranked in their usual order of occurrence after neuroleptic administration):

- Dystonic reactions (hours to days)
- Akathisia (hours to weeks)
- Akinesia or bradykinesia (days to weeks)
- Rigidity (days to weeks)
- Tremors (weeks to months)
- Pisa and Rabbit syndrome (months to years)

Parkinsonism refers to the symptoms but not the presence of **Parkinson's disease** (defined as an idiopathic depletion of do-paminergic neurons in the basal ganglia occurring in a sporadic and familial form). The causes of parkinsonism that are of most relevance to psychiatry are:

- Medication-induced dopamine blockade — neuroleptics are dopamine receptor blockers (the antidepressant amoxapine and several antiemetics — prochlorperazine, metoclopramide, promethazine, trimethobenzamide and thiethylperazine also have this effect)
- Medication-induced dopamine depletion, which occurs with reserpine and tetrabenazine
- Lithium, disulfiram, methyldopa and some of the calcium channel blockers
- Toxins such as carbon monoxide, cyanide and methanol

Other extrapyramidal symptoms are:

- **Pisa syndrome**, so named because patients' posture bears a resemblance to the Leaning Tower of Pisa, is a **tardive dystonia** that causes a torsion spasm of torso muscles
- **Rabbit syndrome**, an alternating perioral movement resembling the action of a rabbit's mouth often with lip smacking; this is more rapid and regular than the oro-facial-bucco-lingual movements of **tardive dyskinesia**

<u>X</u> — **Tardive Dyskinesia (TD)** is an involuntary movement disorder associated with prolonged neuroleptic use. *Tardive* refers to

the delayed onset, which occurs from months to years after starting medication. **Dyskinesia** is a distortion of voluntary movement. TD is composed of **choreoathetoid** movements but is considered separately due to its importance in psychiatry. TD occurs in three main areas of the body:

Facial & oral movements (present in 75% of those affected)
- Facial expressions — frowning, grimacing
- Lips and mouth — puckering, lip smacking
- Jaw — chewing, teeth grinding
- Tongue — tremor, protrusion, rolling

Extremities (present in 50% of those affected)
- Choreoathetoid movements in the limbs
- Tremors or rhythmic movements may be present
- Range from rapid, purposeless and spontaneous to slow and complex motions

Trunk (present in 25% of those affected)
- Twisting, rocking or gyrating of the back, neck, shoulders or pelvis

In its early stages TD can easily be missed. It is usually reported by friends or family members who notice the repetitive movements (often smacking or chewing). TD can be passed off as gum or tobacco chewing or even ill-fitting dentures. It is more pronounced during stressful periods and with use of non-affected body parts. Lessening of the movements is seen during periods of relaxation, use of the affected parts, and voluntary suppression. TD is typically absent during sleep. An increase in neuroleptic dosage temporarily improves TD whereas the use of an **anticholinergic agent (ACA)** can actually worsen TD. In severe cases, TD can cause irregularities in speaking, breathing and swallowing. Swallowing air **(aerophagia)** can lead to chronic belching or grunting. Limb involvement can leave patients incapacitated. Risk factors that increase the likelihood of TD occurring are:

- Advancing age and female sex
- Duration of neuroleptic administration
- Increasing neuroleptic dosage
- Presence of a non-psychotic disorder
- Drug holidays (these are not "summer trips" to Amsterdam, but planned discontinuations of medication)

A research instrument was designed to assess the presence of TD. It is called the **Abnormal Involuntary Movement Scale (AIMS)**. The AIMS involves both observation and asking the patient to perform actions. TD is not rare and is worth taking the time to detect. Up to 5% of younger patients who take traditional neuroleptics for one year have at least one finding. This increases to 30% in elderly patients. TD-like movements have been reported in patients with schizophrenia who have never taken neuroleptics. TD has also been proposed to be a late complication of schizophrenia spuriously associated with neuroleptic administration, though there have been legal issues stemming from a lack of **informed consent**.

XI — Tics are involuntary, sudden, rapid, recurrent, non-rhythmic, stereotyped, irresistible movements or vocalizations. Tics generally mimic all or part of a normal movement and may be seen as "purposeful" in this regard. They can range from simple to complex though their duration is often usually only a couple of seconds. Most patients with tics have a unique repertoire that varies in type, location, degree and frequency. Tics often occur in paroxysmal bouts.

Patients can voluntarily suppress tics though this becomes increasingly uncomfortable. Prior to a tic occurring patients may experience premonitory urges or sensations. As with compulsions a feeling of relief comes with expression of the tic. Stress, fatigue, new situations or even boredom can exacerbate tics. Other illnesses, concentration on other matters, relaxation, alcohol and orgasm can diminish tics. Like other movement disorders, tics are virtually absent during sleep. Some simple motor tics are:

- Blinking or **blepharospasm**
- Facial twitches, grimaces, head jerking
- Shrugging or rotation of the shoulders
- Grinding teeth **(bruxism)**

Examples of complex motor tics are:
- Head shaking, jumping, kicking
- Hitting or biting oneself
- Touching or smelling objects

Examples of simple vocal tics are:
- Coughing, humming, grunting, gurgling
- Throat clearing, clicking, clacking
- Sneezing, sniffing, snorting, snuffling

Examples of complex vocal tics are:
- Utterances of inappropriate syllables or words
- **Copralalia** (saying or shouting obscenities)
- **Palilalia** (repeating one's own phrases)

Tics occur in a wide variety of conditions:
- Physiologic tics — mannerisms or gestures
- Primary tic disorders (e.g. Tourette's disorder)
- Chromosomal abnormalities (e.g. Down syndrome)
- Medications (e.g. stimulants used to treat ADHD)
- Head trauma and cerebral infections (e.g. encephalitis)
- Intellectual disabilities
- Neurologic conditions (e.g. Huntington's disease)
- Schizophrenia

XII — Tremors are involuntary movements consisting of regular, rhythmic oscillations of some part of the body. They are usually seen in the hands, arms, head, neck, lips, mouth or tongue, but can also occur in the legs, voice or trunk. Causes of tremors most relevant to psychiatry are:

- Stress-induced — situational anxiety, anxiety disorders (e.g. panic disorder), strong emotions, fatigue and hypothermia
- Psychotropic medication-induced — lithium, valproate, neuroleptics, various antidepressants, etc.
- Familial or physiologic tremors
- Neurologic or endocrine disorders

<u>XIII</u> — Negative Symptoms

Part of developing skills as an interviewer is to pay attention to what is being said or done, but also to learn what is *not* being said or done (and probably should be). For example, patients who talk about their families while omitting certain members (like a sibling) often reveal the presence of a conflict. Similarly, there are certain behaviors that are remarkable for their absence instead of presence.

Many clinicians divide the signs and symptoms of schizophrenia into **positive** and **negative symptoms**, also referred to as **Type I** and **Type II** schizophrenia, respectively. One way to conceptualize this distinction is that positive symptoms are "added" to the picture (they are not present in unaffected people) while negative ones are deficits in the clinical presentation (features that are expected to be present). **Positive symptoms** are: **hallucinations**, **delusions**, **formal thought disorders**, and **bizarre** or **disorganized behavior**. A mnemonic for negative symptoms is as follows:

"NEGATIVE TRACK"

Negligible response to conventional antipsychotics
Eye contact is decreased
Grooming & hygiene decline
Affective responses become flat
Thought blocking
Inattentiveness
Volition diminished
Expressive gestures decrease

Time — increases the number of negative symptoms
Recreational interests/Relationships diminish
A's — see below for the 5 'A's in the SANS Scale
Content of speech diminishes (poverty of thought)
Knowledge — cognitive deficits increase

• When Kraepelin and Bleuler first described schizophrenia they made distinctions between fundamental (positive) and accessory (negative) symptoms. By the way, Bleuler suggested the term schizophrenia in 1911 to refer to a "splitting of the mind" or schism between thoughts and feelings, and thoughts and behavior. Prior to this Kraepelin called the condition **dementia praecox**.

• Negative symptoms are less effectively treated by antipsychotic medications (positive symptoms respond more favorably), particulary typical or first generation agents. Newer antipsychotics (atypical, second and third generation) appear to treat negative symptoms more effectively.

• Dr. Nancy Andreasen developed standardized scales to assess the presence of positive and negative symptoms. The scale for positive symptoms is called the **SAPS (Scale for the Assessment of Positive Symptoms)**. The other is the **SANS (Scale for the Assessment of Negative Symptoms)**. The major components in the SANS scale are contained in the following mnemonic:

a**P**athy
a**L**ogia
 Affective flattening
a**N**hedonia
a**T**tentional deficits

'**PLANT**' mnemonic for the five A's from the *Scale for the Assessment of Negative Symptoms* was provided by:
Dr. David Wagner, Indianapolis, Indiana

4. Cooperation & Reliability

What Factors Determine Cooperation & Reliability?

Patients' cooperation is required so that the information they provide is useful in forming diagnostic impressions. Some patients can't or won't share information (the distinction is important to make). The degree of cooperation offered by patients needs to be made clear early in the presentation of the MSE since it colors the rest of the information obtained. In a sense, cooperation refers to the *quantity* of information given. Cooperation is probably best gauged by the responses patients give to open-ended questions, which allow them relatively unstructured opportunities to say what is on their minds. Most patients share information freely and participate readily in interviews. Of course, a cornucopia of information is not useful unless it is accurate. In a similar vein, reliability refers to the *quality* of data obtained in the interview. The following parameters provide a way of assessing cooperation and reliability:

- **Eye Contact** (Section I)
- **Attitude/Demeanor** (II)
- **Attentiveness to the Interview** (III)
- **Level of Consciousness** (IV)
- **Affect** (V)
- **Secondary Gain** (VI)

How Do I Describe the Various Aspects of Cooperation & Reliability?

I — Eye Contact is a universal indicator that someone is interested (in something anyway). Continued eye contact generally indicates cooperativeness, but can be a sign of hostility as well. Patients may avert their gaze momentarily to think about something. Sustained aversion of gaze can indicate that the patient has encountered an area of difficulty. Eye contact is variously described as *continuous, good, intermittent, fleeting* or *absent*.

II — Attitude/Demeanor towards the interview and interviewer is another important element of cooperation. Patients may have biases from previous contact with mental health professionals. This usually becomes obvious early in the interview and can pose a significant obstacle to obtaining information. Such biases are most commonly seen with patients who:

- Have personality disorders (typically borderline or antisocial)
- Are under duress to attend the interview
- Suffer from chronic conditions that have resulted in numerous contacts with different caregivers
- Have an agenda **(secondary gain)** to carry out
- Are cognitively impaired due to medical illnesses or substance ingestion/withdrawal

Demeanor can be described as being *cooperative* or *uncooperative*. Cooperative patients can be further described as:

- *Obsequious/Solicitous/Effusive*
- *Seductive/Flattering/Charming*
- *Over-inclusive/Eager to please*
- *Entitled/Controlling*

The manner in which patients are uncooperative requires elaboration. For example:

- *Hostile/Defensive*
- *Suspicious/Guarded*
- *Antagonistic/Critical*
- *Childish/Regressed*
- *Sullen/Withdrawn*

To illustrate your description more precisely, it helps to include a quote or observation from the interview.

III — Attentiveness to the Interview impacts on the degree of cooperation and reliability. Patients can be distracted by external (e.g. noise) or internal stimuli (e.g. hallucinations) while speaking. Further, they may preferentially pay attention to these events and not see the point of answering your questions. Interest can diminish in an interview for any number of reasons:

- Patients with certain personality disorders often become bored in interview situations
- Patients experiencing a manic or hypomanic episode may be so distractible that they cannot sustain focus on your questions
- Delirious patients drift in and out of lucidity
- OCD can cause patients to succumb to the intrusive thoughts or the irresistible urge to reduce their state of anxiety; they may also engage in a number of ritualized behaviors
- Patients who are psychotic may experience hallucinations or can incorporate material from the interview into their delusions and this reduces their ability to pay attention to your questions

These findings are recorded in the MSE as patients being attentive or inattentive. A further description is given for diminished attention span. Reasons might include:

- Being preoccupied
- A reduced or fluctuating level of consciousness
- Being distracted by activity in the interview
- Sudden shifts in affect or mood state

IV — Level of Consciousness (LOC) refers to the degree of alertness or level of arousal. In typical interview situations patients are alert, attentive to their surroundings and responsive to questions. This can be recorded in the MSE as *"the patient was fully alert and attentive to the interview."*

Aberrations in the level of arousal are important to include early in the recording or reporting of the MSE. The reader or listener needs to be aware of this at the outset because an altered level of consciousness affects the quality of the information that follows. A diminished LOC immediately calls into question the possibility of a serious medical condition and warrants urgent investigation.

<u>**V**</u> — **Affect** is defined as:

- The observable quality of an emotional state
- The moment-to-moment variability of visible emotions based on what is occurring in the interview (external events) or feelings (internal events)
- The range of reactions to questions that would usually be considered to be of emotional significance

A financial analogy is as follows: affect is like the minute-to-minute variation in the value of a company's stock while mood is the general trend over a longer time period. Another analogy is that affect is to weather as mood is to climate.

Affect and mood are presented in Chapter 8 (page 87). In situations where intense affect interferes with obtaining information, describing it in the *Cooperation & Reliability* section helps put subsequent information into perspective.

<u>**VI**</u> — **Secondary gain** refers to an actual or real-world advantage that patients derive from being ill. Common examples include:

- Being relieved of occupational responsibilities
- Obtaining prescription medications (often for drugs that have an habituating potential or street value)
- Avoiding military service
- Gaining leverage in personal relationships
- Postponing examinations
- Transfer out of prison or jail
- Shelter and/or food
- Financial gain

In psychoanalytic theory a symptom functions to decrease intra-psychic conflict, which is called **primary gain**. **Tertiary gain** is used to describe the advantage that others receive from the patient's illness, such as disability income supporting an entire family.

What Is the Relevance of "Gain" to the MSE?

Malingering is the conscious production of physical or psychiatric symptoms for secondary gain. Someone skilled in describing psychiatric symptoms can be so convincing that it is not possible to tell if he or she is actually experiencing what is being described. For this reason, mental illnesses are often favored by malingerers. **Factitious**

disorder is the deliberate production of symptoms (physical or psychological) in the absence of secondary gain. Symptoms are produced so that patients present as being genuinely ill. The motivation is thought to be for **primary gain**, however, there may be secondary gain that is not immediately obvious.

5. Speech

Which Aspects of Speech Are Important?

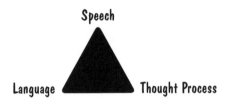

Speech refers to verbal expression and consists of utterances, words, phrases and sentences.

Language refers to the communication of comprehensible ideas. Not all speech can be considered language (e.g. vocal tics, campaign promises). Language can be conveyed by means other than speech — posture, gestures, expressions, actions and sign language all transmit clear meaning without requiring verbal expression. Language consists of ideas (usually expressed as words) that convey meaning **(semantics)** and are properly produced **(articulation)**.

Thought process refers to the way ideas are produced and organized. Thought is inferred from speech and language (including writing or signing) because it cannot be assessed directly. Thought and language have a large interplay but do actually describe different processes. Language is the principal means by which thought process is expressed. Animals and pre-verbal humans readily demonstrate that thought occurs without the ability to express syntactical language.

While humans are anatomically capable of speech, language is an acquired ability. Understandable sounds and words are uttered by eighteen months of age, while phrases are spoken between two and three years of age.

Assessing speech abnormalities begins with the following:

1. Is the patient's speech abnormal?
2. In what way is it abnormal?
3. Was the patient's speech ever normal?
   - If not, consider one of the conditions affecting the acquisition of normal language skills (listed below)
4. Is anything else abnormal in addition to speech?
   - Reading
   - Comprehension
   - Copying
   - Ability to follow directions
   - Writing/Drawing
   - Repetition
   - Naming

Given that speech is encoded thought, the chance to hear patients speak gives us valuable clues about their mental functioning. It is not unusual to have a patient present for an interview who is shabbily dressed and acting in an eccentric manner. While you are busy (prematurely) considering a diagnosis of a serious mental illness, you are taken aback by the person's intelligence and eloquent speech once he or she begins talking.

Which Conditions Affect the Acquisition of Normal Language Skills?

- Intellectual Disability
- Autism Spectrum Disorders
- Communication Disorders

Distinguishing Medical From Psychiatric Causes of Speech Disturbance

Distinguishing between aphasias and disorders of thought process can be difficult because they both affect verbal expression. In the case of severe psychiatric disturbances it may not be possible in one interview to make this distinction. A classic example of this is the differentiation of speech abnormalities in psychosis from true aphasia. The following is a list of potential distinguishing features:

Parameter	Medical	Psychiatric
• Greater severity	+	−
• Continuous duration	+	−
• Abrupt onset	+	−
• Older age of onset	+	−
• Related language symptoms	+	−
• Word finding difficulties	+	−
• Awareness of difficulty (partial)	+	−
• Loss of repetition, naming, and comprehension abilities	+	−

What Are the Specific Aphasias?

Because of the potential difficulties in distinguishing primary language disorders from psychiatric conditions, the aphasias will be summarized here. The reason that it is vital to make this distinction is that aphasias almost always involve injury to the dominant cerebral hemisphere, which requires urgent intervention. Psychiatric conditions are generally not medically urgent and involve significantly different forms of treatment. Aphasias are usually classified as **fluent** or **nonfluent**. Further distinction is made using three tests:

- **Comprehension** — tested by the ability to follow simple, and later, more complex requests
- **Repetition** — tested with simple and complex phrases
- **Naming** — tested with common and uncommon objects

An alternate system for classifying aphasias is as **receptive** or **expressive** based on the ability to understand and speak, respectively. This system poses difficulties for non-neurologists because both receptive and expressive deficits are frequently present patients with aphasias.

Paraphasias (paraphasic errors) are substitutions of letters or words for the intended word. There are four types:

- Related (approximative) — *light* is used instead of *lamp*
- Unrelated (semantic) — *caboose* is used instead of *lamp*
- Literal (phonemic) — *lump* is used instead of *lamp*
- Neologistic (jargon) — *piloknarf* is used instead of *lamp*

Nonfluent Aphasias
- Broca's
- Transcortical Motor
- Global

Fluent Aphasias
- Wernicke's
- Transcortical Sensory
- Conduction
- Anomic

What Other Qualities of Speech Are There?

<u>I</u> — **Accent & Dialect** are terms used interchangeably to describe regional or cultural differences in pronunciation. Accent can be used to refer to the speech of patients who are not native English speakers (e.g. French, Spanish, German, Italian accents). Dialect can be used to describe regional variations in those who are native anglophones.

There are five major dialects in the U.S. — New York, New England, Southern, Appalachian and Western. In Canada, those from the Atlantic Provinces have the most distinctive style of speech, while the rest of the country has a "middle American" accent. In the UK, the skill in distinguishing dialect is finely honed. Britons can often make educated guesses as which side of the street someone lived on while growing up in a village or hamlet.

II — Amount of speech varies widely in interview situations. Mental health professionals spend years learning how to obtain and organize information. Patients are given considerable leeway for what constitutes a "normal" amount of speech (recorded as *responsive, spontaneous, well-spoken* or *fluent*). Anxious patients provide extraneous detail through their desire to be helpful. Other patients feel inhibited, provide sparse answers and offer little information spontaneously.

Terms used to describe an increased amount of speech are: *verbose, loquacious, talkative, copious, logorrhea, vociferous, overabundant* or *expansive*. The amount of speech can be increased in:

- Mania (see **pressure of speech** below)
- Anxiety disorders
- Personality disorders
- Fluent aphasias

Terms used to describe a decreased amount of speech are: *paucity of speech, impoverished, laconic, taciturn, single-word answers* and *minimally responsive*. The amount of speech can be decreased in:

- Major depressive disorder
- Schizophrenia (particularly as a **negative symptom**)
- Avoidant, dependent and schizoid personality disorders
- Dementia (especially the early stages) or delirium

At one extreme, **pressure of speech** describes patients who are driven to keep talking and have both an increased rate and amount of speech. A key feature of pressured speech is that it is not usually interruptible.

The other extreme involves the absence of speech, which is called **mutism**. This is found in neurologic conditions and very severe forms of psychiatric illnesses (particularly major depressive disorder and schizophrenia).

<u>**III**</u> — **Articulation** refers to the clarity with which words are spoken. This is not a description of word-finding ability or eloquence of speech. Words can be poorly pronounced due to:

- Slurring (e.g. drug toxicity, alcohol ingestion)
- Mechanical problems (due to poorly fitting dentures, missing teeth **(edentulous)** or chewing gum)
- Tardive dyskinesia

Terms used to describe this are: *garbled, slurred, mumbled, clipped, choppy, unclear* or *poor diction*.

<u>**IV**</u> — **Modulation** is the loudness or softness of speech. Some patients are naturally louder when they speak, while others add emphasis at various points in the interview. Conditions where patients speak louder than normal include:

- Mania/hypmania
- Psychotic disorders
- Cluster B personality disorders (see page 26)
- Dementia

Conditions where modulation is reduced include:

- Major depressive disorder
- Personality disorders (i.e. avoidant or schizoid)
- Medical disorders
- Substance intoxication or withdrawal

<u>**V**</u> — **Pitch**, as in music, refers to the highness or lowness of spoken words. Pitch usually varies throughout the course of a sentence. For example, it rises when questions are asked and falls when authoritative statements are made. Pitch also changes with emotional state (e.g. rising with anxiety and falling with despondency). A point of interest is that pitch range can be altered by psychiatric illnesses, particularly psychotic and dissociative disorders.

VI — **Spontaneity** is the degree of engagement in the interview. Information volunteered without a question being posed is called *spontaneous speech*. **Latency** refers to the interval of time taken to answer questions or connect sentences.

VII — **Rhythm** or **cadence** varies in normal speech to add emphasis and maintain interest. Certain rhythm disturbances exist:

- **Stuttering** — repetition of certain syllables
- **Cluttering** — a nonfluent disruption involving bursts of rapid speech containing syntactical errors; the articulation is poor and the speaker is unaware of the speech abnormalities
- **Scanning speech** — a nonfluent abnormality where there are irregular pauses between syllables as if each one was "scanned" separately prior to being pronounced
- **Inflection**, or stress, adds an extra communicative element to speech, contributing to the pragmatics of language

Patients with **aprosodias** miss the finer messages conveyed with emphasis in speech. In many instances, non-native speakers, patients with subnormal intelligence and those who cannot think abstractly **(concrete thinking)** also miss the meanings conveyed by inflection. These occurrences do not constitute aprosodias.

6. Thought Form/Process

What is Thought Form/Process?

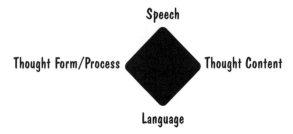

Speech

Thought Form/Process   Thought Content

Language

Speech refers to any form of verbal expression. With aphasias, speech is produced with deficits in fluency, repetition, comprehension, prosody, etc.

Language is the exchange of comprehensible ideas and describes the communicative value of speech.

Thought content describes *what* is being talked about and is presented in the next chapter (Chapter 7, page 77).

Thought process or **thought form** refers to the way in which ideas are organized. This is an assessment of *how* patients are communicating. The degree of connection between ideas and the flow of thought is disrupted in many psychiatric illnesses. When such disruptions occur they are referred to as **thought disorders**. The way that ideas are linked together is as important as their content. Because thought cannot be accessed directly it is assessed via speech, sign language, written materials and behavior.

What Constitutes A Disorder of Thought Form?
The following parameters describe thought process:

- Goal directedness

- Tightness of the associations (degree of connectedness) between words, phrases, sentences and paragraphs
- Rate, pressure and rhythm
- Idiosyncrasy of word usage

Thought process is easiest to assess when patients are given open-ended questions. Here, they must decide:

- What is important to say
- How directly will questions be answered
- How much detail to give and when to move on
- How to move on to another topic and the degree of connectedness to what was just being discussed

In a closed-ended style of interview, disorders of thought process may be missed. However once it is apparent that a thought disorder is present greater structure in an interview may be the only way of moving on to more salient areas.

The individual disorders of thought process (listed in order of increasing severity) are:

- **Circumstantial Thought** (Section I)
- **Tangential Thought** (II)
- **Flight of Ideas** (III)
- **Rambling** (IV)
- **Loose Associations** (V)
- **Thought Blocking** (VIa)
- **Thought Derailment** (VIb)
- **Fragmentation** (VII)
- **Verbigeration** (VIII)
- **Jargon** (IX)
- **Word Salad** (X)
- **Incoherence** (XI)

Process Disturbance	Nature of Disturbance
Circumstantiality/ Tangentiality	• tight linkage between ideas • sentence structure is maintained • overinclusive of detail (circumstantiality) or does not address the point (tangentiality)
Flight of Ideas	• sentences are maintained • ideas remain connected • rapid and frequent shifts in topic
Rambling	• clusters of sentences remain goal-directed but are interspersed with groups that are not
Loose Associations	• sentences are maintained • phrases and sentences are still properly constructed • the connection between ideas is unclear or nonsensical
Thought Blocking Thought Derailment	• syntax remains intact but speech suddenly halts (blocking) and then shifts (derailment) • patients may or may not return to the previous topic, and are unaware that a block has occurred
Fragmentation	• words are intact but phrases become disconnected
Verbigeration	• repetition of words and phrases
Jargon	• syntax remains intact but speech becomes meaningless
Word Salad	• words are intact, all syntax is lost
Incoherence	• words are unintelligible, speech is garbled or dysarthric

What Is Considered Normal When It Comes to Thought Process?

People express varying degrees of coherence and detail at different times, so thought process must be considered in conjunction with other features of the interview. Someone who is anxious may speak quickly and provide a lot of information. Some people make great leaps in thinking before verbalizing anything and the connections between their statements may need to be explained. It can be valuable to record segments of the interview to illustrate the patient's thought process. At the end of the interview make a determination about the overall ability of the patient to communicate his or her difficulties. Descriptions that are commonly used to describe thought form are as follows:

- **Tightness of thought**
  well-organized, tangential, loosely connected or *incoherent*

- **Flow of speech**
  spontaneous, hesitant, interrupted or *halting*

- **Directness of replies**
  informative and relevant, embellished or *overinclusive*

- **Flow of ideas**
  logical and with variability, restricted or *repetitive*

- **Vocabulary**
  descriptive, restricted or *idiosyncratic use of words*

- **Flow of information**
  good exchange, adequate, vague or *disorganized*

Thought is normally goal directed. In order to visualize the various disorders of thought process, the following representation will be used:

A•B•C•D•E•F•G•H•I•J•K•L•M•N•O•P•Q•R•S•T
where:

- Each letter represents a word
- The alphabetical sequence indicates proper syntax
- Progression from left to right indicates a logical sequence

The following promotional statement can be schematized using the above substitution of letters.

Rapid Psychler produces humorous and educational books.

▼	▼	▼	▼	▼	▼
A	B	C	D	E	F
▼	▼	▼	▼	▼	▼
noun	verb	adjective	conj.	adjective	noun

A thought process disorder brings about substitution with incorrect words though the syntax remains correct.

Rapid Cycler publishes books about quick bicycle repairs.

▼	▼	▼	▼	▼	▼	▼
G	H	I	J	K	L	M

Here the words have an alternate set of letter designations because they are different than those in the original statement. Since the grammar is correct the letters remain in alphabetical sequence. In another example of a thought process disorder, a sentence that doesn't follow the rules of grammar appears as follows:

Rapido Cyclerista but clear hofic around then upward.

▼		▼	▼	▼	▼	▼	▼
Q		X	V	♣	P	U	Z

Because 'hofic' isn't a word, it is represented by a symbol (**neologisms** are explained later in this chapter).

Thought Process Illustrated

Understanding thought process abnormalities can be made easier with the use of illustrations. The convention used in the following sections is as follows:

The interviewer poses a question, which is shown with the left ellipse.

 The path the patient takes to answer the question

Question Posed ────────────────▶ **Answer Given**

(degree of goal-directedness) is shown by the arrow.

The goal or answer to the question is the ellipse on the right.

I — Circumstantial thought contains an overly detailed amount of information that provides a lot of digressive, extraneous detail in order to give everyone within listening distance a firm grasp of all the relevant or even quasi-relevant factors so that the point, when finally reached, is clearly made with substantive evidence. The preceding sentence is an example of circumstantiality! It could just as easily be defined as speech that contains an excessive amount of detail but does finally reach the point.

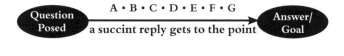

Circumstantiality involves understandable words used in a proper grammatical sequence, but with unnecessary detail. The key feature is that the point is finally made or the question answered. Circumstantiality is most commonly seen in:

- Normal conversations; it is endemic in digressive professors, politicians, many lawyers and some authors
- Obsessive-compulsive/narcissistic personalities
- Temporal lobe epilepsy
- Hypomanic or manic episodes
- Anxiety disorders
- Substance ingestion, particularly with alcohol or stimulants

<u>II</u> — **Tangential thought** remains logical and the direction can be followed. Proper words and grammar are used. The distinguishing factor is that the person does not make a point or answer your question. Tangentiality may help move a conversation along but in an interview situation it may be a sign of pathology. The severity and frequency of tangential speech needs to be gauged to determine if it impacts on the quality of the interview. Tangential replies often stay in the "ball park" of the answer. Patients in whom tangentiality is not pathological can refocus their replies to the question at hand when requested to do so.

Example: "Why did you buy your car?"
"My car has 4 cylinders. It gives me good gas mileage in the city but not much passing power on the highway. I live near a highway and have a garage for my car. I keep it inside even in the summer because sunlight makes the red paint fade."

Tangential thinking is most commonly seen in:

- Personality disorders where verbal communication is maintained principally for the sake of feeling connected to someone, e.g. histrionic and dependent personalities
- Cognitive disorders such as delirium or dementia
- Hypomanic and manic episodes
- Anxiety disorders
- Substance ingestion and abuse (alcohol, stimulants, marijuana, etc.)
- Schizophrenia, though other disorders of thought process are more typical for this illness

III — **Flight of ideas** is non-goal directed speech that "takes off" from the topic at hand. Patients are usually distractible and change topic frequently. Speech remains logical and the connections between ideas are still recognizable. Patients don't elaborate on their ideas before moving on. Their statements contain proper words and grammar. Flight of ideas differs from tangential speech in that topic changes are more abrupt, more frequent and are often prompted by a word in a previous sentence.

A · (B) · (C) · (D) · (E) · (F) · (G) · (H) · (I) · (J)

Question Posed

Answer/ Goal

Example: "Name the Seven Dwarfs"
"Happily, I don't think on such a small level. Small things come in good packages. I cut myself opening my mail yesterday, it still stings. I got stung by a bee last summer, but it's only fair, since I eat honey. I have breakfast every morning because it is the most important meal of the day. I like to eat three squares when I can, but not out of a can. Cans keep food around for years even if you take the label off. I bought a labeling machine, and now everything in my house has a proper name. I like to address my property on a first name basis. Ah, the joys of ownership!"

An examination of these sentences reveals discernible connections between them with a word acting as a trigger for the abrupt and frequent changes in topic. The brackets demonstrate that there are actually connections between ideas.

Note that the word or idea on the right side of the page is the connection between the two statements above and below it:

"Happily, I don't think on such a *small* level."

] small

"*Small* things come in good *packages*."

] packages

"I cut myself opening my *mail* yesterday,
it still *stings*."

] sting

"I got *stung* by a bee last summer,
but it's only fair, since I *eat* honey."

] eating

"I have *breakfast* every morning because
it is the most important meal of the day."

] eating

"I like to eat *three squares* when I can,
but not out of the *can*."

] cans

"*Cans* keep food around for years,
even if you take the label off."

Flight of ideas is most commonly seen in:

- Mania and hypomania; flight of ideas with pressured speech is one of the cardinal signs of these mood states
- In severe mania patients speak in an uninterruptible monologue and head off on numerous tangents
- Patients often pick up on something happening around them to start their flight of thought; in this example, "happily" was a partial answer to the question, since 'Happy' is one of the Seven Dwarfs
- Flight of ideas can also be seen in psychotic disorders (e.g. schizophrenia, brief psychotic disorder, drug-induced psychosis), delirium and dementia

IV — **Rambling** describes speech composed of clusters of related sentences that are goal directed, but then become interspersed with loosely associated statements. It is characteristic of an acute, coarse (non-localized) brain disorder. Rambling is not as severe as loosening of associations but lacks the discernable connections between ideas seen in flight of ideas.

V — Loose Associations

Association refers to the logical connection or "tightness" between ideas. In loose associations a disintegration of meaningful connections between ideas occurs. Proper words, phrases and sentences are still used. Bleuler outlined four terms that started with the letter 'A' as cardinal symptoms of schizophrenia. They are affective flattening, autism, ambivalence and disturbances of association.

Example:
If the example paragraph that illustrated flight of ideas is used with every second sentence deleted (and some further editing), the following series of statements remains:

"Happily, I don't think on such a small level."

                                                   ] ?

"I cut myself opening my mail yesterday."

                                                   ] ?

"I have breakfast every morning."

                                                   ] ?

"Cans keep food around for years."

                                                   ] ?

"I address my property personally."

There is no discernable connection between these sentences at all. Loosening of associations is characteristic of the thought process during psychosis. However, mania can also become so severe that the connection between ideas is lost.

A Comparison of Thought Process Disorders

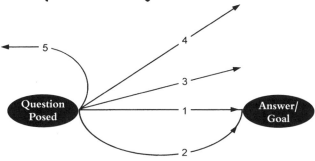

1. Goal-directed logical thought that both addresses the point and answers the question directly.

2. Circumstantial thought contains a mass of digressions, subsidiary clauses and "talking around" the point. People are sometimes aware of their wordiness and that their style of speech (thought) impedes reaching the goal directly.

3. Tangential thought is not goal directed though it starts out being relevant and generally stays in the vicinity of the topic. The point or question is not ultimately addressed, which distinguishes this from circumstantiality. If the thought process does not reach the goal and is overly detailed it can be described as both tangential and circumstantial.

4. Flight of ideas takes off more quickly and radically than tangential speech. Rapid, uncensored associations are made due to significant distractibility and a sense of pressure to keep talking. This is also a form of accelerated speech.

5. Loosening of associations is the loss of meaningful connections between words and phrases. Transitions between topics are not based on logical connections between ideas.

<u>VIa</u> — **Thought blocking** is the sudden involuntary interruption of thought (and speech). It is not the same experience as requiring more time to generate a reply or being too emotionally overwhelmed to continue answering questions. Thought blocking is described as having an idea removed from consciousness or losing one's train of thought. A similar interruption in thinking and movement occurs during petit mal (absence) seizures. Thought blocking is one of the **negative symptoms of schizophrenia**, and is considered a form of **alogia**.

<u>VIb</u> — **Derailment** occurs when speech begins again after an episode of thought blocking. Patients usually begin talking again, sometimes after only a few seconds, but on a different topic. Patients do not usually know what they were speaking about before the thought block and are unaware of the change in topic. Their speech is otherwise fluent and grammatically correct. Thought derailment is one of the **positive symptoms of schizophrenia**, and constitutes a **formal thought disorder**.

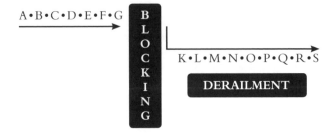

Example: "How about those Orioles?"
"I think they're the team this year! They made some important changes in the off season...I've got to catch that midnight train to Georgia."

<u>**VII**</u> — **Fragmentation** is the loss of meaningful connections between words and phrases. Fragmented speech lacks focus, consisting mainly of phrases that are unrelated. The phrases themselves still have proper syntax and are composed of understandable words. This type of abnormality is similar to Broca's aphasia in its broken delivery. However, in fragmentation, the speech contains the connecting words, articulation is intact, and pauses are not notably long.

A•B•C•D•E . . . I•J•K . . . O•P•Q•R•S•T . . Y•Z

Example:
"The flames of desire. . . viva love. . . ten below zero. . . confessions of a fool. . . singer not the song. . . the ship of the sea sick sailor... I believe in love. . . brighter than the sun. . . kiss me goodbye."

Fragmentation is not specific for any particular condition. It can be seen in psychotic disorders, mood disorders with psychotic features, dementia, delirium, etc.

<u>**VIII**</u> — **Verbigeration**, also known as **palilalia**, is the automatic repetition of words or sounds. The tightness of associations in the speech may otherwise be intact.

A•B•C•C•C•C . . . . B•C•C•C•C . . . .

Example: "Where did you park your car?"
"I parked it, it, it, it . . . . . parked it, it, it, it."

This is most commonly seen in catatonia (due to schizophrenia, mood disorders and medical syndromes).

<u>**IX**</u> — **Jargon** also called **jargon agrammatism** or **driveling** is composed of speech that has lost its communicative value. The syntax is preserved in this disorder and speech remains fluent. The repetition of phrases **(perseveration)** or syllables **(verbigeration)** is not prominent.

A•B•C . . . E•L•O . . . P•E•X•D•U•R•P•L•E . . .

Example: "What was the food at McMaster Medical School like?"
"In verbatim, try delayed transparency. Principles fourth at one."

This is most commonly seen in:

- Any of the causes of Wernicke's aphasia (e.g. strokes, tumors, head injuries)
- Chronic psychotic conditions with a severe course

<u>X</u> — **Word salad** is an extreme form of loosened associations to the point that words have no connection to one another. The speech in word salad is incomprehensible and resembles the incoherence of a **global aphasia**. The articulation remains intact, delivery is usually fluent and prosody of speech is still present.

Word salad differs from fragmentation in that in word salad there is no connection between individual words. Recall that in **fragmentation** it is the phrases or sentences that are unconnected from each other. Word salad differs from **jargon** in that in word salad there is no preservation of syntax though the content of the speech in both disorders is meaningless.

A•X•Q•D•B•E•B•O•P•A•O•L•S•U•X•P•O•R•V•
T•X•X•W•V•T•Z

Example: "What actually are KFC's secret herbs and spices?"
"At, to, but, not, when, if, that, my, never, fuller, clip."

This is most commonly seen in:

- Chronic, severe schizophrenia
- Advanced stages of dementia
- Delirium

XI — Incoherence (unintelligible, garbled speech) can be caused by:

- Severe dysarthria
- Extensive use of made-up words **(neologisms)**
- Private use of words (words that exist but are used in an incorrect manner)

Other Disorders of Thought Process

- **Punning** (Section XII)
- **Clang Associations** (XIII)
- **Echolalia** (XIV)
- **Perseveration** (XV)
- **Neologisms** (XVI)
- **Non sequiturs** (XVII)
- **Private use of words** (XVIII)
- **Rate abnormalities** (XIX)

XII — A pun is a play on words which is made humorous by involving double meanings or similar sounding-words:

- Santa's helpers are *subordinate clauses*.
- Buddhist to a hot dog vendor: *"Make me one with everything."*

Continual punning can be a thought process disorder. Some patients are compelled to use words for their sounds or alternate meanings (such as homonyms). In flight of ideas, the connections between words or ideas may be based on multiple or abstract meanings.

XIII — Clang associations are made on the basis of sound not syntax or logical flow. This occurs most commonly by rhyming the last word in a sentence. In some cases this is considered a type of **phonemic** or **literal paraphasia** where patients substitute a word that sounds similar to one they just used. For example:

"I have to go, you know. To and fro before the blowing snow."

Clang associations are most commonly seen in mania but also occur in aphasias, schizophrenia and various types of dementia.

XIV — Echolalia has been mentioned earlier in the *Chapter 3 (Behavior)*. It is the automatic repetition of someone else's speech. Echolalia is seen in:

- Catatonia
- Transcortical motor and sensory aphasias
- Dementias

Echolalia is distinguished from **perseveration** in that the words repeated are the interviewer's, not the patient's. Echolalia is distinguished from **palilalia (verbigeration)** in that whole phrases are repeated and not just the last word or syllable.

XV — Perseveration is the automatic repetition of a verbal response despite changing questions. Perseveration can also be a motor disorder where the patient repeats the same action. The repeated group of words is sometimes called a **stock phrase**.

C . . . C . . . C . . . C . . . C . . . C . . . C

Example: "Where did you park your car?"
     "Garage."
"How long have you been in town?"
     "Garage."
"Where should the hospital administrator's office go?"
     "Garage."

Perseveration is most commonly seen in: mood disorders, schizophrenia, catatonia and frontal lobe damage.

<u>XVI</u> — **Neologisms** are made-up words or phrases that have idiosyncratic meanings for patients. Neologisms may be formed by the improper use of word sounds or other perceptual abnormalities. They are also called **jargon paraphasias**. In psychiatric disorders neologisms generally occur in syntactically correct places as if they are words the interviewer should know. Ask patients about unfamiliar terms — you'll either detect a neologism or learn a new word. Additionally, neologisms sound as if they could be words. For example...which from the following list are actually words?

- johmet
- jingo
- meltom
- monad

The first and third words are neologisms that have meanings that only a patient using them would understand. Johmet might be the border surrounding a sheet of postage stamps while meltom could be the wrapping around a sandwich. No sense can be made of these words by breaking them down into their root components.

Neologisms can appear in any of the disorders of thought form listed in this chapter. They are most commonly seen in schizophrenia but can occur in any type of psychotic disorder, dementia and several of the aphasias. Patients are not generally aware that they have used a neologism and are usually willing to explain the term once its use has been pointed out.

<u>XVII</u> — **Non sequitur** is a Latin term meaning *does not follow*. Non sequiturs occur readily in normal speech and thought. If someone gets an idea or is suddenly reminded of something (e.g. *Squirrel!*) he or she may start talking about a topic quite apart from what was just being discussed. The reply itself demonstrates proper grammar and syntax and except for not addressing the question, it is not otherwise remarkable.

Non sequiturs can also be a sign of pathology. Generally they are considered to occur whenever the answer given is unrelated to the question that was posed.

XVIII — **Private use of words** refers to the incorrect use of an existing word. Syntax remains correct but the word is used out of context. It is also called an **unrelated** or **semantic paraphasia**. The word substituted for the correct one is unrelated either in sound or function. For example, *"Yesterday I visited my friend gerund."* Gerund is a word but its use here is of a private nature. It was not substituted for the name Gerard (if it were, this would be a **literal (phonemic) paraphasia**).

XIX — **Rate Abnormalities**

The **rate** of speech, or more correctly the rate of thought, constitutes another disorder of thought process. A rapid rate of speech may be a variant of normal and is frequently seen when patients are anxious (either situational or due to an anxiety disorder).

Pressured speech has a rapid rate with an uninterruptible, intrusive quality as if patients are compelled to keep talking. This is also called **pressure of ideas** or **thought pressure**.

At an average rate reading this sentence takes about 3 seconds — *Rapid Psychler produces humorous and educational publications.*

Pressured speech takes less time and keeps going (and going) — *Rapid Psychler produces humorous and educational books. Using humor is a key component in making clinical material interesting and memorable. . . . . .*

Pressure of speech is one of the principal signs of a manic episode and is accompanied by the sensation of **racing thoughts**. The combination of pressured speech and racing thought is expressed verbally as **flight of ideas**. These features can also occur in anxiety states, use of stimulants and hyperthyroidism. Rate of speech (and thought) varies widely in psychiatric illnesses. Rate tends to vary with the amount of speech and loudness. In mania patients speak quickly, have a lot to say and say it loudly. Depressed patients speak in the opposite manner. Increased rate needs to be distinguished from pressure of speech. Patients who have a rapid rate of speech are interruptible, do not appear compelled to keep speaking, and may be anxious. When asked to do so they are able to slow their rate of speech.

Psychiatric vs. Neurologic Terminology

Psychspeak	Neurospeak
Clang associations (p. 71).	Phonemic paraphasia
Driveling speech (p. 69)	Jargon agrammatism
Neologisms (p. 73)	Jargon paraphasias
Private use of words (p. 74).	Semantic paraphasias
Verbigeration (p. 69)	Palilalia

Thought Process Disorder vs. Aphasia

A thought process disorder generally doesn't interfere with:

- Reading
- Repeating
- Naming
- Copying
- Writing

In thought process disorders neologisms are symbolic (typically replace a noun or verb), repeated and used in a syntactically correct way. In aphasias, neologisms can replace any word (are non-symbolic), are not repeated and occur randomly. Aphasias cause the deletion of connecting words (i.e. articles, prepositions, conjunctions) so that speech consists mainly of nouns and verbs. Patients with thought disorders generally speak fluently and with preserved syntax and prosody.

Thought Process Practice Points

- It can be quite difficult to distinguish **word salad** from **Wernicke's aphasia**; oil and vinegar salad dressing is not usually of any assistance in settling this matter either

- If the associations between someone's thoughts seem loosened, point out the shift in topic to the person and ask what the connection was between the two ideas

- Patients demonstrate loosening of associations when writing as well as speaking

- Although loose associations are considered a cardinal sign of schizophrenia they are also seen in cognitive disorders (delirium and depression), mood disorders (especially severe mania or psychotic depression), and drug intoxication or withdrawal states

- **Thought insertion** or **thought withdrawal** can affect the process of thought by increasing or decreasing (respectively) the number of ideas to express

- **Condensation** is a disorder of thought process in which several concepts are expressed in a unified form; this occurs mainly in schizophrenia and substance use conditions, but sometimes in exclusively male groups

7. Thought Content

Thought content refers to *what* patients talk about in the course of the interview. While it may be tempting to simply record that *"Ms. LB answered the questions I asked her"* the ebb and flow of interviews are strongly influenced by the content of patients' answers.

A key reason why the first few minutes of an interview is best left relatively unstructured is that it allows for an assessment of thought content. Special attention should be given to the topics that patients talk about spontaneously, elaborate on, and what themes develop during the course of the interview.

As stressors or symptoms are elicited, exploration helps guide the flow of relevant material while allowing patients the chance to continue speaking in a relatively unrestricted manner. Interviews that consist of a closed-ended or "laundry list" approach restrict the flow of spontaneous information.

What Constitutes A Disorder of Thought Content?

Thought content is considered pathological when any of the following elements are present:

- **Delusions** (Section I)
    - Paranoid
    - Grandiose
    - Jealous
    - Erotomanic
    - Somatic
    - Passivity and Control

- **Overvalued Ideas** (II)
- **Obsessions** (III)
- **Phobias** (IV)
- **Thoughts of Harm to Self or Others** (V)

Patients experiencing delusions, obsessions or phobias seek attention because their lives or the lives of those around them are significantly disrupted by these symptoms. On the other hand, some patients are quite adept at concealing such experiences and make them difficult to elicit especially during the first interview. The degree of awareness that patients have in understanding that their experiences are abnormal **(insight)** varies widely. Impaired or absent insight is usually a sign of a more serious disturbance and/or a worse prognosis. Additionally, abnormalities in thought content evoke variable emotional responses from patients.

<u>**I**</u> — **Delusions** are one of the cardinal symptoms indicating a serious mental illness though they have been reported to occur in well over fifty psychiatric and general medical conditions. A delusion is defined as a fixed, false belief that:

- Is inconsistent with cultural or subcultural norms
- Is inappropriate for the person's level of education
- Is not altered with proof to the contrary
- Preoccupies the thoughts of the patient
- Is not resisted by the patient
- Ranges from implausible to impossible

The content of delusions ranges from narrow (fragmented) to systematized (generalized) and from situations that are at least possible **(non-bizarre)** to those that are impossible **(bizarre)**. In cases where a patient appears to have a discrete, plausible, but false belief (e.g. *"someone monitors my email"*) it may only be possible to establish the presence of a delusion when collateral information becomes available. Cultural differences can also account for unusual ideas. In order to distinguish a delusion from other aberrations of thought content it is crucial to establish that it is indeed fixed. For example, someone who is confabulating or is being deliberately misleading will generally change some part of his or her history when asked to repeat the details later in the interview.

Delusions that start *de novo* are called **primary delusions**. **Secondary delusions** arise out of a mood state, perceptual abnormality (including sensory deprivation or impairment), social factors or other pre-existing psychopathology.

Delusional patients demonstrate altered reasoning processes. **Apophony** (from the Greek *to become manifest*) is the phenomenon in which arbitrary or false ideas are considered fact without adequate proof. This is also called **delusional intuition**. Events and objects become imbued with an overwhelmingly personal significance.

Delusional patients make sweeping inferences based on small amounts of information (the process of **generalization**). They do not use their knowledge or experience to modify their beliefs. For example, a patient who passes through a police radar trap (without speeding) would become convinced that "surveillance" was arranged so the police could monitor his or her actions. Delusions become a psychological compromise and help to make sense of the internal chaos with which patients must contend (a process called **consolidation**).

How Do I Ask About Delusions?

Formulating questions about delusions constitutes one of the most difficult interviewing tasks. As opposed to patients with phobias or obsessions, delusional patients usually don't recognize that they are ill. Asking, *"So, are you delusional?"* probably won't work, necessitating a more refined approach.

1. Look for themes during the interview.
Despite the complexity of mental illnesses, most delusions fall into a fairly small number of themes. Non-bizarre delusions consist of the following types: paranoid, somatic, grandiose, jealous and erotomanic.

2. Questions to help detect the presence of delusions:
  • *"Do you spend a lot of time thinking about one or two things?"*

- *"Do you have some ideas that you hold very strongly?"*
- *"Do others frequently disagree with your point of view?"*
- *"What is it that is most important to you?"*

Because delusions dominate patients' thoughts, these questions are likely to reveal some aspect of delusional thinking if it is present. When patients mention something that could be of a delusional nature, respond with curiosity. An interested, conversational manner is your best strategy to elicit more information.

3. Questions to explore delusional material:

- *"How do you know (that this is going on)?"*
- *"How did this situation start?"*
- *"Why would someone want to do this to you?"*
- *"How do you account for what has happened to you?"*

Regardless of an interviewer's skill, delusions can't always be elicited. Patients with an awareness that others don't share their ideas **(preserved insight)** or who have been hospitalized because of delusional thinking may conceal their ideas. Over time some patients learn to conceal their delusional ideas in order to avoid hospital admission or other psychiatric interventions.

Mood Congruence & Ego Syntonicity

The terms **mood-congruent** and **mood-incongruent** are applied to delusions and hallucinations (which are features of psychosis) that occur with mood disorders. Themes of guilt, worthlessness, death, failure, hopelessness, punishment, illness, etc. are congruent with depression. If the delusional content is along these lines, then the term *mood-congruent* is applicable.

In manic episodes, mood-congruent delusions involve themes of power, brilliance, wealth, longevity, achievement, special relationships or connections, knowledge, etc. Manic patients with delusions of nihilism, poverty or inadequacy have *mood-incongruent delusions*, as would depressed patients with delusions of grandeur, omnipotence, or connections to famous people. Mood-incongruent delusions are a poor prognostic sign and might indicate that schizoaffective or schizophreniform disorder is present.

The term **egosyntonic** is used to refer to symptoms that are not foreign or distressing to patients themselves. Patients generally do not experience delusional thoughts as disturbing. The delusional beliefs become accepted as reality and are therefore egosyntonic. For example, paranoid patients are not disturbed by their continual thoughts of persecution. Instead, they accept that the world is this way and are ever vigilant for evidence to confirm that they are being conspired against or oppressed.

II — Overvalued ideas differ from delusions in that they are less firmly held and their content may be less absurd. Beliefs become *overvalued* in that they preoccupy the patient's thinking and alter behavior. Examples of overvalued ideas are *superstitions* or *magical thinking*. A superstitious (as opposed to delusional) person will concede that walking under a ladder isn't really likely to change one's luck, but he or she just feels better not doing such things. Situations where delusions seem probable but are not clearly present are recorded as overvalued ideas.

III — Obsessions are thoughts, impulses, or images that are:

- Recurrent and persistent
- Unwanted (called **ego-alien** or **ego-dystonic**)
- Not simply an exaggerated degree of concern over current problems
- Recognized as a product of the patient's own mind; obsessions are generated from *within* as opposed to from *without* (in **thought insertion** ideas are imposed from without)
- Not able to be controlled by the person's will
- Recognized as absurd and irrational
- Resisted, at least at some point and to some degree

Obsessive Themes

Like delusions, obsessions tend to fall into a relatively small number of themes:

Theme	Obsession
Cleanliness	Contamination
Order	Symmetry, Precision
Sex & Aggression	Assault, Sexual Assault, Homicide, Insults
Doubt	Safety, Catastrophe, Unworthiness

How Do I Ask About Obsessions?

Obsessions are recognized by patients as absurd and distressing yet they are not expressed as dominantly in interviews as are delusions. Suggestions for inquiries are:

- *"Do you experience repetitive thoughts that you can't stop?"*
- *"Do your thoughts feel like they are your own?"*
- *"Are you ever forced to think about something against your will?"*

Preoccupations are another component of thought content. They differ from obsessions in that they are a willful return to thinking or conversing about a topic. **Ruminations** are another term for intellectual obsessions. Here, people "chew" (mull over) their "cud" (thoughts) but reach no resolution nor initiate a plan or action. For those around the patient there is often an irritating and unnecessary quality (both in time and extent) to obsessive thinking.

<u>IV</u> — **Phobias** are marked and persistent fears that are:

- Viewed by the patient as excessive and unreasonable (phobias are **ego-dystonic**)
- Clearly circumscribed (the person has clearly demarcated objects or situations that are feared)

- Accompanied by a sense of anxiety upon exposure or the thought of exposure to the object(s) or situation(s)
- Capable of causing sufficient distress so that patients go to great lengths to avoid anxiety-provoking stimuli
- Of generally benign objects or situations; for example, fears of a rabid raccoon or a dangerous neighborhood are justified, while a fear of numbers or paper clips is not

Categories of specific phobias and social phobias can be recalled with the following mnemonic:

"ASP & BOAS"

Animal type — e.g. killer chihuahuas
Situational type — e.g. bridges, tunnels, flying, etc.
People (social phobia) — e.g. public speaking

Blood/Injection (this is relatively self explanatory)
Other — used when other categories just won't do
Agoraphobia — avoidance of places where escape or getting help are difficult (see below)
Surroundings — elements in the natural environment such as storms, water, heights, etc.

Agoraphobia is a condition that deserves special mention. The word is derived from Greek and means "fear of the marketplace." The DSM-5 describes it as: *marked fears about specific places or situations from which escape might be difficult or in which help may not be available in the event of having an incapacitating or embarrassing symptoms; the fear is out of proportion to the actual danger posed* (DSM-5, APA, p. 217-8).

Agoraphobia is a common phobia and the one that causes the greatest impairment of social and occupational functioning. Generally, patients who experience repeated panic attacks become "phobic" of the places where attacks occur or in situations where help or escape would be difficult to arrange. Patients who have a moderate-to-severe course of panic disorder frequently have some degree of agoraphobia. They frequently need to be seated near the exit on a bus or in a movie theater. Patients with agoraphobia make constant demands on friends and family members to accompany them on outings. Patients can become housebound if others cannot oblige their requests or if the illness becomes too severe.

How Do I Ask About Phobias?

Phobias are not usually difficult to ask about because they are **ego-dystonic** and patients recognize them as troubling. Unless patients fear something in the room, phobias are not likely to cause significant anxiety during the interview. The presence of phobias can also be inferred through behavior. For example, someone who avoids the public acceptance of an award may have social anxiety disorder (social phobia) or agoraphobia. Suggestions for questions to screen for the presence of phobias are as follows:

Specific Phobias:
- *"Are there objects or situations that make you intensely anxious if you cannot avoid them?"*
- *"Do you make a special effort to avoid certain objects or situations?"*

Social Phobias:
- *"Do you have strong fears about being humiliated in public?"*
- *"Do you have strong or persistent fears that you will do something embarrassing in front of strangers?"*

Agoraphobia:
- *"Do you require special arrangements to be made for you to be comfortable when you are outside of your home?"*
- *"Do you have such a strong sense of anxiety that someone must be with you before you can leave your house?"*

<u>V</u> — Thoughts of Self-Harm
Key risk factors to consider in assessing suicidal risk are as follows:

"SOS MADE PLAIN FOR A DR."

Sex (gender)
Occupational status
Stress level

Mental illness
Age
Drug abuse (substance misues)
Effects of medication (side effects)

Precipitants
Lethality of method
Antidepressants
Isolation
Note written (or a will/testament recently changed)

Family history
Organic conditions — medical illness
Relationship difficulties

Akathisia

Dates (anniversary reactions — see below)
Repeated attempts

Patients who have lost parents to suicide may not only suffer from
anniversary reactions but may also be involved unconsciously in
a self-destructive process at the same age as the parent who died.
Some of the most difficult stressors are:

- Death of a spouse/family member/salesman
- Divorce/separation
- Serious medical illness
- Being fired or retiring from work

8. Affect & Mood

Affect is the visible, external or objective manifestation of an emotional state. It is a record of the momentary dynamic changes in the expression of emotional responses. Both internal (e.g. memories, ideas) and external events (e.g. aspects of the environment) can change affect.

Mood is the person's internal feeling state. It is described by the patient (subjective) and refers to the pervasive emotional tone displayed throughout the interview. Mood changes are less connected to internal or external stimuli and occur less spontaneously. Mood is considered the "emotional background" whereas affect is the "emotional foreground." Affect can be likened to one's degree of satisfaction with the various aspects of a meal, while mood is the overall enjoyment of the entire evening.

What Are the Various Aspects of Affect?

- **Type/Quality** (Section I)
- **Range/Variability** (II)
- **Degree/Intensity** (III)
- **Stability** (IVa)/**Reactivity** (IVb)
- **Appropriateness** (V)
- **Congruence** (VI) — to Mood (VIa)
  — to Appearance (VIb)
  — to Behavior (VIc)

<u>I</u> — **Type** or **quality** is the predominant emotion expressed:

- Happiness
- Surprise
- Interest
- Sadness
- Shame
- Disgust
- Fear/Anxiety
- Anger
- Contentment

<u>II</u> — **Range** or **variability** is the extent to which emotions vary during the interview. A "normal" affective tone consists of any number of the types of emotions listed above.

At some point in the interview a patient would be expected to show some manifestation of emotion. A **narrow** or **restricted** range of affect describes patients who express few emotional states. This can be seen in mood disorders (manic patients can have a narrowly high range), schizophrenia, paranoid disorders and obsessive-compulsive personalities. A **wide** or **expanded** range is seen in cluster B personalities, dementia and substance use.

<u>III</u> — **Degree** is the extent or **intensity** to which emotions are expressed. This can also be called **amount** or **amplitude**, and is a measure of the energy expended in conveying feelings. Affective expression occurs along a continuum:

Low Intensity	Normal	High Intensity
flattened	appropriate	exaggerated
constricted	responsive	dramatic
detached	adequate	passionate

Patients can have an intense affect with a narrow range (e.g. mania or depression). Conversely, a wide range of expression with low intensity is also seen (e.g. histrionic personalities lack a degree of depth to their affective states). **Blunted affect** is a term often used to describe low or flattened intensity. Oyebode/Sims (2014) uses the term to describe a lack of emotional sensitivity to others.

A flattened intensity of affect can be seen in schizophrenia, conversion disorder **(la belle indifférence)**, dementia, and even obsessive-compulsive and schizoid personalities. A heightened degree of affect can be seen in mania, narcissistic or borderline personalities and anxiety disorders. Depression has a variable presentation — some patients convey intense distress while others are muted and seem apathetic.

<u>IVa</u> — **Stability** is the duration of an affective response. Some emotions exist only as long as a facial expression, others are pervasive throughout the interview. Normally affect shifts during interviews

and such shifts are sustained for a few moments and are appropriate to the context of the interview. If changes in affect are small or nonexistent during the interview (called **fixed** or **immobile**) this observation would more properly be considered a description of mood. However, affect is an objective description of how the patient appears to the interviewer. The term **labile** describes affective changes that occur rapidly and frequently. These changes can take place in either the **intensity** or **range** of affect. For example, a patient may be moved from tears to euphoria within seconds (range) or from mild to intense irritation (degree).

IVb — Reactivity of affect refers to the degree to which external factors influence emotional expression. Another parameter of lability is whether or not patients appear to be in control of their emotions. In general, patients with mood disorders, substance intoxication or withdrawal or dementia have less control over their affective states. Patients with personality disorders have a greater degree of control. Lability of affect is commonly seen in the following conditions:

- Cluster B personalities
- Delirium and dementia
- Disruptive, impulse-control and conduct disorders
- Intoxication with drugs or alcohol
- Mania (affect can vary rapidly, e.g. from elated to irritable)

V — Appropriateness is the degree to which visible emotions match thought content. This is also gauged by the degree to which you can empathize with patients. Affect is either **appropriate** or **inappropriate** to the topic being discussed. For example, a patient who smiles when discussing the death of a parent may be displaying an inappropriate affect. If you later learn that this parent was abusive, then this person's smile is more understandable and the expressed emotion is more appropriate to the situation. Inappropriate affect occurs most frequently in schizophrenia, which can cause patients to exhibit a detached demeanor and lose the ability to relate to others.

In schizophrenia, emotional responses are not what would typically be expected for the topics being discussed. Patients can demonstrate what is called **silly** or **fatuous affect** when they giggle, laugh or mock interviewers. Inappropriate affect is also seen in:

- Malingering
- Conversion disorder
- Substance misuse
- Depression

VI — Congruence between affect and other factors in the MSE is another important consideration. The association between affect and the following parameters is as follows:

VIa — Mood
Affect may or may not be congruent to the patient's mood state. For example, depressed patients may still smile and joke. A lack of congruity can be seen in **malingering** or **factitious disorder**, the presence of two separate conditions (e.g. a mood disorder and a personality disorder), substance use, schizoaffective disorder or a psychotic component to a mood disorder.

VIb — Appearance
Emotional disturbances are often manifested in various aspects of appearance because patients have little time or interest in attending to the finer points of grooming and attire. Depressed patients often neglect their self-care, are disheveled and may even dress in darker colors. Manic patients dress flamboyantly and often use poor judgment in picking new looks or styles. Patients with schizophrenia can make bizarre alterations to their appearance and become unkempt.

VIc — Behavior
Facial expression is a key component of affect. Unvarying movements are seen in depression and schizophrenia, while in mania and certain personality disorders expressions are exaggerated. Body movement also indicates affective tone. Patients who are depressed move slowly and infrequently; patients who are hypomanic or manic exaggerate movements and have trouble curtailing their activities.

What Are the Various Aspects of Mood?

Mood is evaluated according to the following parameters:

- **Quality/Type** (Section VII)
- **Reactivity** (VIII)
- **Intensity** (IX)
- **Stability/Duration** (X)

<u>**VII**</u> — **Quality** of mood is the patient's reported emotional state. The DSM-5 includes the following as pathological mood states:

- Depressed
- Angry/Irritable
- Euphoric
- Anxious

Depressed mood occurs when patients feel less energetic, hopeful or capable than what is usual for them. This mood state can be described by many qualifying terms such as: *sad, blue, worthless, guilty, flat, hollow, miserable, gloomy, glum, forlorn, morose, troubled, exhausted, somber, brooding, unhappy, subdued* or *withdrawn*. Because depression is used to refer to mood disorders these mood states are often referred to as **dysphoric** (meaning a state of unhappiness or feeling ill at ease). Depressed mood is a diagnostic criterion for the following disorders (among others):

- Major depressive disorder
- Persistent depressive disorder (dysthymia)
- Depressed phase of bipolar I and II disorders
- Cyclothymic disorder
- Trauma and stressor-related disorders (adjustment disorders)

The diagnosis of a mood disorder rests on associated features, severity (degree of social and occupational impairment) and duration. Major depressive episodes can be a complication of any other psychiatric condition. The term **double depression** refers to an episode of major depression complicating dysthymia. Depressed mood can be such a long-standing experience that it becomes characterological. Depressed mood is often accompanied by changes in:

- Appearance (decline in self-care)
- Behavior (few spontaneous movements)
- Speech (speak softly and have little to say)
- Affect (restricted range, variable intensity)
- Thought content (morbid themes)
- Thought form (significant latency in responses)
- Diminished cognitive functioning

Euphoric mood occurs when patients feel energized, elated or ecstatic. This is to a greater degree than what is experienced when patients are "feeling high" or in a "good mood." Some of the terms used to describe euphoric mood are: *up, flying, grand, uninhibited, omnipotent, buoyant, jovial, racing, driven* or *on top of the world.* Euphoric mood is seen in:

- Mania/hypomania
- Dementia and delirium
- Schizophrenia (usually with marked disorganization)
- Substance misuse (particularly with stimulants)

When patients are experiencing a dysphoric mood they frequently seek help for the way they feel. When patients are euphoric they rarely present for assistance and often have to be brought to medical attention because of the impact their mood state is having on others or on their social/occupational functioning.

Angry/Irritable moods do not constitute discrete disorders, but are frequent complications of other conditions. Some of the following terms are used to describe these mood states: *annoyed, miffed, pissed off, seething, sharp, disgruntled, cranky, indignant, incensed, bellicose, smoldering, exasperated, furious, ill-tempered,* or *easily provoked.*

Irritability or anger are often seen in:

- Mania/hypomania
- Cluster B personality disorders
- Disorders where paranoia is prominent
- Substance misuse, particularly withdrawal syndromes
- Delirium or dementia
- Intermittent explosive disorder

Irritability is defined as being easily provoked to anger. The DSM-5 lists irritability as one of the three mood states seen in mania or hypomania. Irritability can often be present when a manic or hypomanic episode becomes severe.

Anxious mood can occur normally, especially if patients are unfamiliar with or intimidated by the interview process. It is to be expected that patients will be anxious about such areas as diagnosis, prognosis and treatment implications. Anxiety is pathological when it is pervasive or present to a degree that interferes with social or occupational functioning. Terms used to describe an anxious mood are: *fearful, tense, edgy, worried, nervous, uptight, frazzled, petrified, uneasy, rattled, terrified* or *paralyzed.* Anxiety is prominently seen in:

- Phobic disorders
- Panic disorder
- Generalized anxiety disorder
- Obsessive-compulsive disorder
- Posttraumatic stress disorder
- Adjustment disorder with anxiety

Anxiety can complicate any other psychiatric condition and is a common symptom in many medical conditions.

<u>VIII</u> — **Reactivity** is the degree to which mood is altered by external factors. Mood can be changed by events or interactions with others. Manic patients often escalate with stimulation. Depressed patients may feel worst in the morning. Anxious or angry patients have fluctuations in their mood. In the past depression was divided

into **endogenous** and **reactive** types based on the presence of a (presumed) precipitant. The endogenous aspect is now a subtype of depression called the **melancholic features specifier**. In this type of depression there is a lack of mood reactivity to usually pleasurable stimuli. Another subtype of depression, called the **atypical features specifier** contains two criteria related to mood reactivity:

- Mood brightens in response to positive events
- A long-standing pattern of **interpersonal rejection sensitivity** (not limited to episodes of mood disturbance) resulting in significant social or occupational impairment

Depressed patients with melancholic features have a greater likelihood of responding to medication or ECT. Atypical features are most often seen in women and younger patients and frequently only a partial recovery from these episodes is reported. Atypical features may indicate bipolar depression or a seasonal component.

IX — Intensity refers to the degree to which the mood is expressed. Like affect, mood has depth, quality and amplitude. Two patients can experience depressed mood with a similarly flat affect and restricted range of emotional expression. One may appear lethargic, withdrawn and show little interest in the interview. The other patient may have problems with concentration, lowered self-esteem and be able to convey the degree to which this episode has interfered with his or her life. The difference between these patients is the depth or intensity of their mood state.

X — Stability or duration describes the length of time the mood disturbance exists without significant variation. Mood disorders are required to have a specific minimum time course:

• Major depressive episode	2 weeks
• Manic episode	1 week
• Persistent depressive disorder	2 years
• Cyclothymic disorder	2 years

How Do I Ask About Mood Symptoms?

Mood symptoms are usually distressing to patients and they speak about them or display them readily in interviews. Since mood is a subjective phenomenon, patients need to be asked about their emotional state.

- *"How have you been feeling lately?"*
- *"How would you describe your mood right now?"*
- *"I'd like you to rate your mood on a scale from 1 to 10. If 1 is the worst you've ever felt, and 10 is the best, what score would you give yourself right now?"*

Some patients will answer feeling questions with thinking answers, e.g. *"I feel that the Orioles will win the World Series"* or *"I feel like a pizza"* are not considered statements of mood. It may be necessary to point out a patient's reactions as a means of eliciting information about mood, e.g. *"You looked very sad when you were talking about being ripped off at the drive-thru. How were you feeling at that time?"* As with affect, incongruities between reported mood state and observable signs need to be explored.

A difficulty commonly encountered in interviews is being able to distinguish mania/hypomania from the elevated mood states that most people experience from time to time. The following questions can help make this distinction:

- *"Was your mood ever so high that friends or family members thought you needed to get help?"*
- *"Did you get yourself into serious financial, legal or relationship trouble when your mood was high?"*
- *"Did your mood ever become so high that you thought you had supernatural powers, connections to celebrities or revolutionary ideas?"*
- *"Did your mood ever get so high that people around you said that you were doing things that were really out of character for you?*

9. Perception

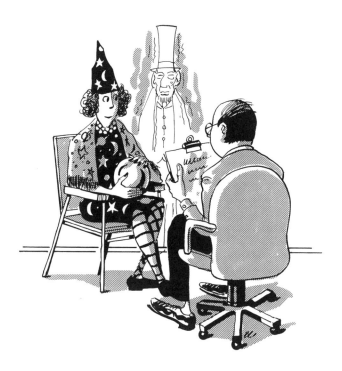

Perception is the process of experiencing the environment and recognizing or making sense of the stimuli received. An object in the environment causes a **sensation**, which upon interpretation by the brain becomes a **perception**. Disorders of perception involve false associations or the arrival of a percept without a stimulus. While imagination can bring about perceptions in any sensory modality there is normally no difficulty in distinguishing one's fantasies from actual external stimuli. Patients experience perceptual abnormalities as clearly as they do reality, but have lost the ability to distinguish a perception's source.

What Are the Various Aspects of Perception?

- **Hallucinations** (Section I)
- **Illusions** (II)
- **Disturbances of Self and Environment** (III)
    depersonalization, derealization
- **Disturbances of Quality or Size** (IV)
    micropsia, macropsia, dysmegalopsia
- **Disturbances in the Intensity of Perception** (V)
    hyperacusis, visual hyperaesthesia
- **Disturbances of Experience** (VI)
    déjà vu, jamais vu

<u>I</u> — **Hallucinations** are perceptions that occur when there is no actual stimulus present. They are the most severe of the disorders of perception. Additional features of hallucinations are that they:

- Occur in all sensory modalities
- Can be simple or complex
- Seem as vivid as real life experiences
- Occur spontaneously
- Are often intrusive (as are obsessions)
- Are internal experiences attributed to external sources

Hallucinations occur in the following sensory modalities:

Sense	Name of Hallucination
sight	visual
sound	auditory
smell	olfactory
taste	gustatory
touch	somatic/haptic

Brief, poorly formed experiences are called **incomplete**, **unformed** or **elementary hallucinations**. Examples are flashes of light, whispered sounds, faint odors or being gently nudged.

• **Auditory hallucinations** are the most common type in psychiatric conditions. In general, they occur as voices that speak clearly formed words, sentences or even have conversations. In medical conditions, they are more like **elementary hallucinations** involving indistinct sounds such as ringing, grating or humming. Auditory hallucinations are one of the cardinal symptoms of schizophrenia and are part of the criteria for schizophreniform disorder, schizoaffective disorder, brief psychotic disorder, and psychotic disorder due to another medical condition. Patients are usually able to describe their "voices" in some detail. They are aware of the gender of the hallucinatory voice and sometimes it is someone they are familiar with. In some instances, patients are instructed by a voice to perform an act, which is called a **command hallucination**. The repetitive nature of these commands can be too much to bear and patients may take action in an attempt to stop the hallucinations. Auditory hallucinations are usually derogatory and critical towards patients. Experiencing the non-stop cacophony of insulting, belittling comments is one of the tortures of mental illness. Hallucinations are one of the **positive symptoms of schizophrenia** and are usually diminished by antipsychotic medications. Auditory hallucinations can also consist of machine-like sounds, music or animal vocalizations. In contrast, auditory hallucinations in medical conditions tend to be elementary or incomplete and have a shorter duration than those in psychiatric illnesses.

• **Visual hallucinations** are the next most prevalent type present in psychiatric illnesses. It is more common to have visual and auditory hallucinations occurring together than it is to have visual hallucinations alone. One such combination involves auditory hallucinations with partial or inferred visual hallucinations. For example, a patient who hears a voice coming from the coat rack may also see or "might have seen" arms gesticulating as "it" was speaking. Isolated visual hallucinations should prompt an investigation for a medical cause (such as an illness or the effects of substance use). When visual hallucinations occur exclusively in psychiatric conditions they are often the result of a psychotic disorder. Visual hallucinations can be simple or complex. They can be as brief as a vision or as involved as having a visit from President Abe Lincoln. **Extracampine hallucinations** involve experiences beyond the normal sensory range (e.g., being able to look out a window in Detroit and see someone in St. Louis). Visual hallucinations can also form or be part of delusional thinking. A patient who "sees" a menacing Viking in her hospital closet may develop delusions of persecution. Paranoia often causes people to believe that they see their persecutors in public places or just outside of their homes.

Oneiroid states (from Greek, meaning *dream-like*) occur in schizophrenia and delirium. Patients experience vivid hallucinations, which can range from terrifying to engrossing. Oneiroid states can become an alternate world. Patients can keep track of oneiroid states and reality at the same time. The **Charles Bonnet syndrome** is a rare condition consisting of formed, complex, repetitive visual hallucinations (that are recognized as such). There are no symptoms of other psychiatric conditions, no clouding of consciousness and no hallucinations in other sensory modalities in this condition.

• **Olfactory hallucinations** are far less common than the auditory or visual types and their presence warrants medical investigation. These hallucinations can occur in:

  • Patients with psychotic disorders

- Patients with coexisting psychiatric disorders and epilepsy
- Patients with comorbid psychiatric and medical problems

Unfortunately, olfactory hallucinations rarely involve pleasant smells. The most common smells are burning rubber, rotting garbage or strong body odors. These smells often are of personal relevance to patients. Smell is the sense most closely linked to memory and these hallucinations are often accompanied by strong feelings. The olfactory association areas are in the frontal lobes and limbic system (hypothalamus and amygdala). Olfactory hallucinations accompany hallucinations in other modalities as well as delusions. For example, patients with somatic delusions (*"I am rotting inside"*) may have accompanying olfactory hallucinations.

- **Gustatory hallucinations** involve more than just having unusual taste in matters. These are the least common type and occur in the same group of conditions as do olfactory hallucinations. Patients who believe they are being poisoned may experience unusual tastes. Like olfactory hallucinations these are rarely pleasant — often being described as metallic, acid, bitter or some bizarre combination of tastes. Psychotropic medication can have an effect on taste sensation. Common examples are: lithium (metallic), zopiclone (metallic) and disulfiram (garlic-like).

- **Somatic hallucinations** are made up of three types:

   1. Kinesthetic hallucinations are sensations of moving body parts such as joint position, body rotation, etc.

   2. Cenesthetic or **visceral hallucinations** involve internal organs (*"The long axis of my spleen has now aligned itself parallel to the equator"*)

   3. Tactile hallucinations involve disorders of bodily sensation, such as:

    formication — the sensation of insects crawling on the skin
    haptic — the sensation of being touched
    hygric — involves shifts in fluid (*"My thymus is full of lymph"*)
    thermal — temperature related (*"My ear lobes are burning"*)

Tactile hallucinations occur in psychotic conditions, temporal lobe epilepsy and migraine headaches. They are often paired with either **somatic delusions** or **delusions of control**.

Hypnagogic hallucinations occur while falling asleep and **hypnopompic hallucinations** occur upon awakening. These experiences are not considered pathological when they occur alone. They can also occur during illnesses causing dehydration or fever. These hallucinations are usually visual but can be auditory or tactile. While their duration is brief, they can occur as complex hallucinations. Hypnagogic and hypnopompic hallucinations also occur in narcolepsy. Many adults have had the experience of hearing their names called only to find that no one was there. Other brief, familiar sounds are also commonly experienced and are not pathological. **Bereavement** is the reaction to, and grieving process endured, after the death of a loved one. This period is often filled with "hallucinatory" experiences involving the deceased person.

<u>**II**</u> — **Illusions** are *misperceptions* of existing stimuli. Actual percepts are distorted or altered so that they appear as something different but remain within the existing sensory modality (in other words, an object that is visualized does not become transformed into a sound). Illusory experiences are affected by particular factors:

- The need to make sense of the environment, in this way illusions fill in the blanks left by inattention or uncertainty (e.g. misreading a word or being oblivious to a spelling mistake because the reader knew what was meant in the passage)
- Emotional state or expectation; a person who is frightened by walking alone at night is more likely to see a

menacing figure in the shadows than if he or she was with someone or walking the same route in daylight

Pareidolia refers to a type of imagery that persists when looking at a real object. The illusion and real stimulus exist simultaneously but the pareidolic illusion is recognized as unreal. An example of this is seeing faces or shapes in clouds. Such illusions can be so striking that they require little imagination to visualize.

III — Disturbances of Self and Environment

Depersonalization is a change in the perception of self, causing the individual to feel *as if* he or she has become unreal.

Derealization is a change in the awareness or the perception of the external world. It may be difficult to make a clear distinction between the two perceptions because patients may feel themselves blending into the surroundings during an episode of depersonalization. These conditions have the following features:

- They are unpleasant and cause anxiety or dysphoria
- Patients retain an awareness that the experience is unreal
- Typical descriptions involve leaving one's body or somehow being outside of one's self — "looking down at myself from the ceiling" or "watching myself in a movie" are common descriptions of such experiences

A theme of inadequacy is often reported. Patients feel as if they have become barren or incompetent and there is a distortion of time. These experiences occur even in psychologically healthy people.

IV — Disturbances of Quality or Size

Micropsia is the perception of seeing things as being smaller than their actual size. **Macropsia** is the perception of objects seeming larger than their actual size. **Dysmegalopsia** is the perception of seeing one side of an object as being larger than the other (e.g. the faces in some of Pablo Picasso's paintings).

<u>V</u> — Disturbances in the Intensity of Perception

In these alterations sensory input is either augmented or diminished in intensity. For example, **hyperacusis** occurs when sounds are experienced as louder than they actually are. Smell, touch, taste and sight (called **visual hyperesthesia** when enhanced) can all be similarly affected.

<u>VI</u> — Disturbances of Experience

Déjà vu is a French term meaning *already seen* or *there's nothing new in that*. It is used to denote a feeling of familiarity to situations that are novel. **Jamais vu**, meaning *never seen*, is applied to situations that are familiar but strike the person as something they have not experienced. The most common medical cause of these disturbances is temporal lobe epilepsy. Schizophrenia is the psychiatric diagnosis most often associated with frequent or severe experiences of this kind. When pathological, these disturbances are called **identifying paramnesias**. They can cause difficulty with the veracity of memory. Patients may not be able to accurately recall if an event occurred or not. Time perception can also be altered. An **autoscopic hallucination** refers to the experience of seeing oneself as if in a mirror image or projected onto the external world. Recognition is intact and the image is correctly identified by the person. The opposite can also occur, called **negative autoscopy** or

heautoscopy. Here, the person looks in the mirror and sees nothing. These conditions can be a feature of parietal lobe lesions, which can also cause other abnormalities of perception:

- **Anosognosia** — unawareness of having an illness, e.g. non-recognition of one side of the body (hemi-inattention)
- **Prosopagnosia** — inability to recognize familiar faces

Pseudohallucinations

Pseudohallucinations retain the quality of a perception without a stimulus but the person recognizes that the perceived event is not actually occurring. True hallucinations appear to be concrete, real and happening apart from the patient (in their **external** or **objective space**). Pseudohallucinations occur in subjective, inner space. Patients refer to the "inner eye" or "inner ear" as perceiving the stimulus, which is usually auditory or visual. Pseudohallucinations can be vivid and formed. The "pseudo" part refers to preserved insight on the patient's part, it does not refer to poorly formed perceptions (called **elementary hallucinations**). In other words, these experiences are "pseudo" because there is an awareness of their false origin, not because of vague stimuli. In these situations, the patient's **reality perception** is impaired but **reality testing** remains intact.

How Do I Ask About Perceptual Disorders?

Perceptual disturbances, along with disorders of thought content, are usually the most difficult to ask about in interviews. There is an awareness in the general public that delusions and hallucinations make one "crazy" and some patients become offended by questions about these areas. In some cases behavior is altered because patients are responding to hallucinations (e.g. being distracted by having to pay attention to the interviewer's voice while simultaneously experiencing hallucinations). In other situations patients simply won't share their experiences or even have command hallucinations telling them to say nothing to interviewers! When asking about perceptual disturbances indicate that you know they occur and are prepared to discuss them:

- *"Many people with difficulties like yours have other symptoms as well. To be thorough, I'd like to ask you about some of these things to complete my understanding of what's been happening."*
- *"Have you had any unusual experiences?"*
- *"Have things been happening around you that seem puzzling?"*

One of the distinguishing features of hallucinations is that they seem as real as actual perceptions. A key point in establishing this is the **lack of corroboration** (i.e. other people around the patient do not share the experience). If after asking the above questions patients don't share their experiences, you may have to ask more specific questions, such as:

- *"Have you heard a voice from someone who was not in the room?"*
- *"Have you seen something that other people couldn't see?"*
- *"Have you had experiences such as. . . (example of a hallucination) that others didn't share?"*

If the presence of any perceptual abnormality can be established, treat this as you would any other symptom and get as much detail as possible. Questions should assess duration, quality, intensity, variation, associated events, etc.

- *"Did you recognize whose voice it was?"*
- *"Did the voice/voices tell you to do something?"*

The question, *"Did the voice seem to come from inside or outside your head?"* is often asked. The significance of this is that true auditory hallucinations are considered to originate outside the self (e.g. from radio towers). However, true hallucinations can also be perceived as coming from within. Another way of asking this question is to inquire whether the experience felt like a product of the person's mind or whether it was a completely external experience. Other questions can be posed as follows:

- *"Have you ever experienced a taste that wasn't due to something you were eating?"*
- *"Have you ever experienced a strong/bad taste or smell that you couldn't account for?"*
- *"Have you had sensations in your body that felt like they were due to unseen forces?"* (e.g. being touched or moved by some thing, internal organs being shifted, etc.)

10. Insight & Judgment

How Are Insight & Judgment Assessed?

On a basic level, **insight** can be defined as having an awareness of one's illness. A more extensive definition is provided by Markova (1992): *Insight is a form of self-knowledge which includes not only information on problems, but also an understanding of their effect on the way in which the self interacts with the world.*

Insight is not a symptom but a process or a continuum. Inferences are made about a patient's level of insight from other areas of the MSE (i.e. thought content and behavior). While insight is usually recorded as *absent*, *partial* or *intact,* it has important implications for evaluating areas such as: suicidal risk and dangerousness, severity of illness, predicting the response to treatment and treatment adherence. Other matters such as obtaining valid informed consent or determining the need for involuntary committal rely heavily on a patient's degree of insight. Lastly, the term "insight" is used in psychoanalytic literature to describe the process of bringing repressed impulses or emotions into consciousness.

Insight is a cognitive awareness and is technically a component of thought content. Within the limited time frame of the MSE it may be practical to limit the assessment of insight to the following aspects:

- The awareness of having an illness
- An understanding of the factors contributing to the illness
- An appreciation that various signs and symptoms are part of a disease process
- The awareness that one's illness also impacts other people and society at large
- Acknowledgment of the need for treatment

Readers interested in an elegant and comprehensive discussion of insight are encouraged to read the articles by Markova, one of which is listed in the References Section (pages 124 – 125).

Judgment is defined as a process that involves the transformation of uncertainty into a preference. Kaplan (1988) outlines five stages in this process:

1. Appraising the challenge
2. Surveying alternatives
3. Weighing the alternatives
4. Deliberating about selection
5. Making a commitment to a choice

Judgment involves both a *cognitive awareness* (decision) and an *action* (behavior). Intact insight and judgment are the end result of many factors: intelligence, accurate perception (of both internal and external events), absence of significant mood changes, the ability to understand and communicate ideas, intact cognitive abilities, control over impulses and the capacity for abstract thinking.

How Do I Describe Insight?

Full Insight
- Recognizes that signs and symptoms are part of an illness
- Able to modify behavior
- Fully cooperative with treatment

Partial Insight
- Recognizes that there are problems but does not attribute them to an illness
- May understand that others (family, doctor) see them as ill
- Some ability to modify behavior
- Variable cooperation with treatment

Impaired/No Insight
- Denial of illness or that there are problems
- Has no capacity to understand the concerns of others
- Poor adherence or follow-through with treatment

How Do I Gauge Insight?

Many of the aspects of insight are dealt with in the body of the interview. In situations where the degree of insight needs to be specifically addressed the following questions can help with an assessment of insight:

- *"Is it your opinion that you have an illness?"*
- *"How do you account for the difficulties you are/were having?"*
- *"Have you had experiences that you think aren't normal?"*
- *"What does (name of condition) mean to you?"*
- *"What is important to help you with your recovery?"*
- *"What will happen if you don't follow through with the treatment proposed for this condition?"*
- *"What would help you feel better?"*

How is the Degree of Judgment Determined?

Judgment is a process that leads to a decision or an action. In interview situations it can be distilled down to an assessment of what the person did or didn't do with respect to his or her illness. Kaplan (1988) proposes the following approach to gauging judgment:

- What is the patient's understanding of the problem?
- What is the patient's understanding of the doctor's recommendations?
- What is the patient's understanding of the doctor's rationale?
- What is the patient's choice?
- What is the patient's rationale for his or her choice?
- What does the patient anticipate as the consequences of the choice being made?

This protocol contains many of the key elements a clinician would consider in determining the capacity for providing informed consent, and an expanded explanation can be found in Wear-Finkle (2000).

Other factors assisting in determining judgment are:

- The ability to generate an accurate list of pros and cons for a course of action
- The degree to which a patient's actions are in his or her best interests
- The extent to which insight is present
- Adequate contemplation before taking action

Poor judgment can be evidenced by the following actions:
- Impulsivity
- Engaging in actions with a high probability for damaging consequences (regardless of how impulsively they were carried out):
  - shoplifting
  - buying sprees
  - physical assault
  - irrational switching of cola brand
  - promiscuous sex
  - reckless driving
  - vandalism

Although the most important factor leading to sound judgment is adequate insight, the terms are not synonymous. For example, patients with personality disorders may be well aware that their actions cause considerable distress to others yet they do not change their behaviors (despite having at least partial insight). Some patients display good judgment despite having poor insight. For example, some patients take medication because others want them to, not because they are convinced they need it. Other patients visit emergency departments for social reasons when they are ill. While they are in need of help their visit may well be coincidental to the need for treatment.

In the time constraints of the MSE a practical approach to determining judgment focuses on how a patient came to medical attention. If it is not clear ask about how he or she entered the mental health system:

- Did the person seek assistance of his or her volition?
- To what extent were others (e.g. the police) needed to motivate the patient into seeking assistance?
- How long did the person wait before asking for help?
- How bad did things get before help was sought?
- Are there associated medical problems?
- Did others suffer harm because of the patient's actions?
- What was the "final straw" before taking action?

How Do I Ask About Judgment?

In situations where judgment needs to be directly assessed, the following questions may be useful:

- *"What are your plans for the future?"*
- *"What would you do if you became acutely suicidal?"*
- *"What are the first signs you are aware of when things are starting to go downhill? What do you do about them?"*

Proverbs

Proverbs are distilled pieces of wisdom that describe universal human truths, tendencies or concerns. Andreasen (1977) points out that proverb interpretation in the MSE is a time-honored tradition and that some clinicians are so fascinated with asking patients to interpret them that they omit crucial sections. Andreasen (1977) summed up the results of her study as follows: *"At best proverb interpretation may have relatively good validity but poor reliability, and the greatest validity is obtained in those cases when differential diagnosis is not a problem. At worst, therefore, the validity of using proverbs in a clinical situation is somewhat questionable."*

A common criticism of proverbs is that they are highly dependent on culture. Patients who grew up in other countries and whose native tongue is not English may miss the abstract meaning of a proverb leading clinicians to incorrectly conclude that their thinking was overly concrete and underestimating cognitive abilities.

11. Cognitive Functions

How Are Cognitive Functions Tested?

The areas tested in a comprehensive MSE are:

- **Orientation** (Section I)
- **Attention & Concentration** (II)
- **Memory** (III)
     Registration/Immediate
     Short-Term/Recent
     Long-Term/Remote
- **Intelligence Estimation** (IV)
- **Knowledge Base/Fund of Information** (V)
- **Capacity to Read and Write** (VI)
- **Abstraction/Concrete Thinking** (VII)
- **Visuospatial Ability** (VIII)

<u>I</u> — **Orientation** is tested according to the following:

- **Time** (time of day, day, date, month, year, season)
- **Place** (hospital/clinic/office address and floor level, town or city, state, county, country)
- **Person** (identity of the person and recognition of family members, friends, health care providers, etc.)

Orientation is usually lost in the sequence of:
     time (most common) **>** place **>** person (least common)

<u>II</u> — **Attention & Concentration**
Attention is the ability to direct mental energy when fully alert. It is a conscious, willful focusing of cognitive processes while excluding competing stimuli. **Concentration** is the sustained focus of attention for a period of time. Attention is assessed by checking **digit span** (the number of numbers they can recall both forward and backward). You can usually start by testing 4 numbers recited in a forward fashion. Most adults have digit recall spans of between 5 to 7 numbers forward and 3 to 5 numbers backward, without errors and completed within 30 seconds. Read off the numbers so

that there are pauses at least one full second between them. Avoid adding emphasis to the numbers as you read them. Numbers that are grouped too closely or with some rhythm can cause a spuriously good level of recall. For example, many companies have developed jingles so that their phone numbers are more memorable. Another consideration is to avoid using numbers in a sequence (5-6-7-8) or exclusively odd/even numbers.

Concentration is most frequently tested with **serial seven subtractions**. Patients are not allowed to use an aid in this test (even their fingers). You can introduce this as follows, *"I'd like you to start with the number 100 and subtract 7, then from this number subtract 7 again and keep going."* Alternative numerical tests are:

- Subtracting serial threes starting from 20
- Serial additions
- Starting at another number using a different interval of subtraction (e.g. 103 minus 8)

III — Memory
Registration is the instantaneous recall of new information, also called **immediate memory**, and is dependent on alertness and adequate concentration.

Short-term memory has a capacity for about 7 items over 20 seconds, though this can be increased with training. **Recent memory** is sometimes used synonymously but is also used for events that occurred in the past few hours. This information is either discarded or committed to long-term memory. **Long-term memory** has no demonstrable storage limit and provides a patient's **fund of knowledge**. This is also called **remote memory** or **delayed recall** and this type of memory generally remains stable over time.

The most common test of verbal memory involves word recall. This is used to test **immediate memory** (**registration**) and **short-term memory** (**recent memory**). The patient is given a list of three to five words and asked to recall them after about five minutes. The words chosen should have the following characteristics:

- They should be unrelated to each other
- They should not be something in the room or that is shown to the patient
- They should be unrelated to the person's vocation or interests (e.g. don't ask an auto mechanic to remember a lug nut, cam shaft and exhaust manifold)

Other tests of short-term memory are:

- A name, address and zip code for a fictitious person
- A short "story" of three to four sentences having about 25 points of information; an intact response involves remembering approximately 15 of these details
- Word lists of about 15 items which can be related or unrelated; intact recall is considered to be somewhere in the vicinity of 50% of the words (this declines with age)

If a patient cannot remember all of the items it is a common practice to prompt them. This can be done initially by stating the category of the missing item(s) (e.g. "It was a color..."). If this doesn't work, present a list of other words that includes the missing item(s) and ask the person to guess. This provides patients with more help than listing the category. Failing this prompt may indicate a more serious impairment.

Make sure you don't mention the missing item too close to the beginning of the list, and don't add any inflection to your voice when mentioning the correct word. There is no established standard with which to assess performance of short-term memory. If the patient requires prompting or a word list, record this as such. Short-term memory can also be assessed by using **visual design reproduction tests**.

Long–term memory can be assessed in terms of recent events (hours to days) or remote events (years). This can be tested by giving patients questions to which you can verify the answer. For example, the following information is usually readily available:

- Date of birth
- Address, zip or postal code, and phone number
- Previous appointments or hospitalizations
- Medication type and dosage
- Recollection of your name (if you gave it)

<u>IV</u> — **Intelligence** involves:

- The assimilation and recall of factual information
- Logical reasoning and problem-solving skills
- Abstraction, generalization and symbolization

Intelligence can be gauged in interviews by:

- Degree of insight, judgment and abstract thinking
- Fund of knowledge
- Vocabulary (widely considered the best single indicator)
- Level of education, vocation, interests & hobbies

Three distinct types of intelligence have been described: mechanical, abstract, and social. Intelligence is usually reported as an **intelligence quotient (I.Q.)**

$$\text{I.Q.} \quad = \quad \frac{\text{MENTAL AGE}}{\text{CHRONOLOGICAL AGE}} \quad \text{x } 100$$

The most widely used and best standardized intelligence test is the **Wechsler Adult Intelligence Scale (WAIS)**. The current version is the **WAIS–R** (R for revised). By definition, a normal IQ is 100. Intellectual disability is generally considered to be an IQ of less than 70. Superior intelligence is above 120.

<u>**V**</u> **— Knowledge base** can be estimated by incidental factors during the interview or may need to be more fully explored if cognitive deficits are discovered in other areas of testing. Head injuries and dementia are common causes of permanent knowledge deficits. The "pseudodementia" of depression can give the appearance of impaired cognitive functioning because patients tend to answer with *"I don't know"* responses. When pressed to respond they are often able to if sufficient time is allowed. Common questions of general knowledge involve:

- Naming political figures or celebrities
- Significant dates (e.g. world events or conflicts)
- Capital cities, neighboring states, etc.

This information doesn't have to involve the personal significance of the questions used to test remote memory.

<u>**VI**</u> **— Capacity to Read and Write**
Assessment of these basic functions is often omitted in initial interviews. Illiteracy is prevalent at unfortunately high rates and can be masked by people with good verbal skills. It is common for illiterate people to be able to sign their names, which is often all that is required in clinical settings. Having patients write down their names and the date and (later) follow a simple written command helps to screen for deficits. It is also useful to have patients write a sentence on the page.

<u>**VII**</u> **— Abstraction/Concrete Thinking**
Abstract thinking is a complex mental ability. It requires one to think in a multidimensional manner by keeping all the characteristics of a "mental set" in mind and integrating the nuances into a new understanding. In interviews patients demonstrate abstract thinking when they can appreciate all the meanings of an item, list similarities and differences, use logical reasoning and grasp the "whole picture" of a situation.

The opposite of abstraction is **concrete thinking**. This is a literal, unimaginative, narrow understanding of a concept. It is also called **one-dimensional thinking** and is often a feature of intellectual disability. Examples are as follows:

- "Whisky kills more people than bullets."
  abstract — alcohol is deadlier to more people than is gunfire
  concrete — that's because bullets don't drink

Abstraction/Concrete Thinking can be tested with similarities and differences. The **similarities test** involves comparing two objects and listing common qualities. For example, "What are the similarities between a chair and a desk?"

abstract — both furniture, things can be put on them, etc.
concrete — four legs, made of wood, touch the floor, etc.

Abstraction involves function instead of form and the ability to generalize from particulars. The **differences test** requires patients to consider similar objects and list their distinguishing features (e.g. wine goblet vs. coffee mug).

VIII — Visuospatial Functions
This is tested in the MSE by assessing **constructional ability**. Patients are asked to draw a figure (usually geometric) on a piece of paper. The **Mini-Mental State Examination (MMSE)** uses interlocking pentagons for this test. The aspects involved in scoring the drawing are preserving: (i) the sides (ii) the angles and (iii) interlocking corners. Another common test is to have patients draw a cube showing the correct three-dimensional orientation.

The **clock drawing test** has been widely used. Patients are asked to draw a complete clock face and indicate a certain time. Drawings are scored for: completeness (all the numbers), correctness (numbers in the proper place and sequence) and orientation (numbers on both sides and evenly spaced).

The Comprehensive MSE

Appearance Parameters
- Gender & Cultural Background
- Actual & Apparent Age
- Attire
- Grooming & Hygiene
- Body Habitus
- Physical Abnormalities
- Jewelry & Cosmetics
- Tattoos

Behavior Parameters
- Agitation
- Hyperactivity
- Psychomotor Retardation
- Akathisia
- Automatisms
- Catatonia
- Choreoathetoid Movements
- Compulsions
- Dystonias
- Extrapyramidal Symptoms
- Tardive Dyskinesia
- Tics
- Tremors
- Negative Symptoms

Cooperation Parameters
- Eye Contact
- Attitude/Demeanor
- Attentiveness to the Interview
- Level of Consciousness
- Affect
- Secondary Gain

Speech Parameters
- Comprehension
- Repetition
- Naming
- Amount of Speech
- Articulation
- Modulation
- Spontaneity
- Rhythm
- Accent & Dialect
- Pitch

Thought Form Parameters
- Circumstantiality
- Tangentiality
- Flight of Ideas
- Rambling
- Loose Associations
- Thought Blocking
- Thought Derailment
- Fragmentation
- Verbigeration
- Jargon
- Word Salad
- Incoherence
- Punning
- Clang Associations
- Echolalia
- Perseveration
- Neologisms
- Non sequiturs
- Private use of words
- Rate abnormalities

Thought Content Parameters
- Delusions
- Overvalued Ideas
- Obsessions
- Phobias
- Thoughts of Harm to Self or Others

Affect Parameters
- Type/Quality
- Range/Variability
- Degree/Intensity
- Stability/Reactivity
- Appropriateness
- Congruence to Mood

Outline for a Comprhenhensive Mental Status Examination

Mood Parameters
• Quality/Type   • Reactivity   • Intensity   • Stability/Duration

Perception Parameters
• Hallucinations   • Illusions   • Disturbances of Self and Environment
• Disturbances of Quality or Size
• Disturbances in the Intensity of Perception
• Disturbances of Experience

Level of Consciousness/Sensorium Parameters
Alert/Subdued/Rousable/Obtunded/Unconscious

Insight & Judgment Parameters
Full/Partial/Impaired/Absent Insight
Good/Fair/Poor Judgment

Cognitive Functions Parameters
• Orientation   • Attention & Concentration
• Memory   Registration/Immediate
            Short-Term/Recent
            Long-Term/Remote
• Intelligence Estimation   • Knowledge Base/Fund of Information
• Capacity to Read and Write   • Abstraction/Concrete Thinking
• Visuospatial Ability

Endings (Suicidal and/or Homicidal Ideation)
• Sex (gender)   • Occupational status   • Stress level
• Mental illness   • Age   • Drug abuse (chemical dependency)
• Effects of medication (side effects)   • Precipitants
• Lethality of method   • Antidepressants   • Isolation
• Note written (or a will left)   • Family history
• Organic conditions — chronic medical illnesses
• Relationship difficulties   • Akathisia
• Dates (anniversary reactions)   • Repeated attempts

Sample MSE Reports

Example 1

Ms. Manique is a 29-year-old college student brought to the hospital by her roommate. Despite having final exams she had been busying herself with a wide array of activities unrelated to her studies.

Ms. Manique's **appearance** was that of a woman who looks her stated age and is dressed in mismatched clothes, consisting of a suit jacket, yoga pants and hiking boots. In the interview, her **behavior** involved refusing to be seated and speaking only if she was allowed to pace around the room. She rummaged through her purse at the beginning of the interview and then wrote out several lists for the remainder of the time. She was superficially **cooperative** with the assessment and said she'd talk as long as she could continue making her lists and if the interview didn't last more than ten minutes. She was considered **reliable** but biased towards describing the details of her recent activities instead of answering questions.

Her **speech** was loud, rapid and pressured, but remained understandable and had proper syntax. Prosody was exaggerated throughout. **Thought process** involved connections that were generally logical. On two occasions she was unable to repeat the questions posed to her or to relate the connection between them to what she was just saying. The **content** of her thoughts had to do with her plans to start at a senior management level in any Fortune 500 company of her choice after graduation. She thought she had developed powerful insights into the business world and even offered the interviewer an autographed copy of her term paper.

Her **affect** was forceful and exuberant and remained consistently high during the interview. She described her mood as energetic and that she'd never felt better. She gave her mood a score of nine out of ten (she says she'll be a ten after graduation). She denied any **perceptual** problems. She stated she felt well and couldn't see why others were concerned. On this basis, her **insight** and **judgment** were both deemed to be impaired.

Testing of her **cognitive functions** revealed that she was completely oriented. She was able to **register** four items and **recalled** them at around five minutes. However, she could not recall the interviewer's name or her exam schedule, so her **long-term memory** was considered impaired. Her attention and concentration were intact for six numbers forward and four backward. She performed three **serial subtractions** correctly and then told a story about the number seventy-two. She was able to create a considerable list of **similarities and differences** many of which demonstrated a high level of abstraction. Her **knowledge base** was consistent with her level of education and her **intelligence** seemed to be above average.

Example 2

Ms. Lo is a 47-year-old separated woman who is employed as a professional cello player. After missing her third rehearsal she was brought to the clinic when she was eventually found isolating in the basement of her home.

• Her appearance is that of a woman appearing older than her age. She was dressed in a housecoat and slippers. She is thin, has an odor of poor hygiene, and has old scars visible on her left wrist and forearm.

• She sat throughout the interview in an immobile position with her hands at her sides and her head slumped forward on her chest. She made few spontaneous movements while speaking.

• She was uncooperative with the interview and said she wanted to be left alone. The information she shared did seem to be reliable.

• Her speech was fluent and syntactically correct. There was a latency of several seconds before replying to questions. She spoke in a monotonous manner with no variability or prosody.

• Her thought process showed intermittent loosening of associations with periods of rambling when she was asked open-ended questions.

• Her thought content involved delusions of persecution and being infested. On a recent trip overseas she inadvertently knocked over the display of a merchant who was selling rare cultural artifacts. This merchant put a "curse" on her. Ms. Lo has been coping poorly and declining since that time. She is convinced she has some type of flesh-eating organism inside her.

• She has passive wishes to die, but denies that she'd do anything to harm herself. There are no thoughts of wanting to harm others.

• Her affect was flat and showed little range during the interview. She felt doomed and hopeless, and described her mood as "terrible."

• She described perceptual abnormalities in the form of tactile (insects crawling on her skin) and cenesthetic hallucinations (the lining of her intestines was being eroded). She was also constantly harassed by the voice of the merchant she encountered while she was on her trip.

• Her insight and judgment were both considered impaired on the basis of the bizarre delusions, her inability to understand that she is ill, and because she needed others to bring her in for help.

• Cognitive testing revealed that she was only oriented to person, month, year, and season. She knew she was in a hospital, but not which one. She was able to register only one object after two tries and was not able to recall this object after three minutes. Digit span was intact only for three numbers forward and two numbers backward. She did not attempt the serial sevens test. She was able to follow a written command and wrote a sentence (*"I am going to die for what I did."*). In response to many questions she replied, *"I don't know."* Testing of similarities and differences revealed concrete thinking and highly idiosyncratic replies.

In Conclusion

This book has provided you with all of the information you need to do a great MSE. The benefits to your patients and you as a clinician will last for your entire career. The MSE is a sensitive, specific and powerful means of gauging a patient's psychiatric difficulties. As a natural extension of the interview, it can be interwoven so that it isn't left until the end of your interview. I hope you've enjoyed this book and learning about descriptive psychopathology. If you have suggestions for improvements to this book, please contact the publisher via *rapid@psychler.com*.

References

American Psychiatric Association
The American Psychiatric Association Practice Guidelines for the Psychiatric Evaluation of Adults, 3rd Edition
American Psychiatric Association, Arlington VA, 2016
http://www.psychiatry.org/psychiatrists/practice/clinical-practice-guidelines
psychiatryonline.org/doi/book/10.1176/appi.books.9780890426760

American Psychiatric Association
Diagnostic & Statistical Manual of Mental Disorders, 5th Edition
American Psychiatric Association, Arlington, VA, 2013

N.C. Andreasen
Reliability and Validity of Proverb Interpretation to Assess Mental Status
Comp. Psychiatry 18(5): 564 – 472, 1977

D.W. Black & N.C. Andreasen
Introductory Textbook of Psychiatry, 6th Edition
American Psychiatric Publishing, Inc., Arlington VA, 2014

R. Campbell
Psychiatric Dictionary, 9th Edition
Oxford University Press, New York, 2009

A. Conan Doyle
The Complete Sherlock Holmes, Vol.1, p. 352
Doubleday & Co. Inc., New York, 1971

B.J. Sadock & V.A. Sadock, Editors
Kaplan and Sadock's Synopsis of Psychiatry, 11th Edition
Lippincott, Williams & Wilkins, Baltimore, 2014

K.H. Kaplan
Assessing Judgment
General Hospital Psychiatry 10(3): 202 – 208, 1988

D.M. Kaufman
Clinical Neurology for Psychiatrists, 7th Edition
W. B. Saunders Co., Philadelphia, 2013

I.S. Markova & G.E. Berrios
The Assessment of Insight in Psychiatry: A New Scale
Acta Psychiatr. Scand. 86(2): 159 – 164, 1992

D. O'Neill
Brain Stethoscopes: The Use and Abuse of Brief Mental Status Schedules
Postgraduate Medical Journal (69): 599 – 601, 1993

F. Oyebode
Sims' Symptoms in the Mind: Textbook of Descriptive Psychopathology, 5th Ed.
Saunders, London, England, 2014

E. Othmer & S. Othmer
The Clinical Interview Using DSM-IV-TR, Volume 1: Fundamentals
American Psychiatric Publishing, Inc., Arlington, VA, 2002

D.J. Wear-Finkle
Medicolegal Issues in Clinical Practice: A Primer for the Legally Challenged
Rapid Psychler Press, Port Huron, MI, 2000

E.L. Zuckerman
The Clinician's Thesaurus, 7th Edition
Clinician's Toolbox, The Guilford Press, New York, 2010

Index

The Author

Dave Robinson is a psychiatrist practicing in London, Ontario, Canada. His particular interests are outpatient adult psychiatry and in developing educational programs for a diverse range of audiences. He was the lead author for the Mental Health chapter in the 2013 Canadian Diabetes Association Clinical Practice Guidelines and will reprise this role for the 2018 version as well.

The Artist

Brian Chapman was born in Sussex, England and moved to Canada in 1957. He was formerly a Creative Director at Mediacom. He devoted almost 20 years of his time and talents to create over one-thousand illustrations for Rapid Psychler Press. Brian passed away in 2012 after a brief respiratory ailment. His extreme generosity and legendary sense of humor live on in the pages of this book.

Rapid Psychler® Press

Rapid Psychler Press was founded in 1994 with the aim of producing textbooks and resource materials for mental health education. Rapid Psychler Press has a library of images for use in presentations.